3,00

American Studies in the United States

American Studies In the United States

A Survey of College Programs

By

ROBERT H. WALKER

Chairman, Committee on American Studies Programs
The American Studies Association

LOUISIANA STATE UNIVERSITY PRESS

Baton Rouge

Milligan College Library
Milligan College, Tennessee

E
973.175.8
W185a
.W33

Copyright 1958 by Louisiana State University Press

Library of Congress Catalog Card Number: 58-13398

Lithoprinted in U. S. A. by Edwards Brothers, Ann Arbor

Contents

CHAPTER ONE   A HISTORY OF THE SURVEY   1

CHAPTER TWO   A SURVEY OF AMERICAN STUDIES
                      ACTIVITY   6

                      A Directory to American Studies
                      Courses and Programs in
                      Colleges and Universities   7

                      Directory Supplement 144
                         Variations on American
                             Studies 144
                         Summer "Refresher" Programs . 146
                         New Programs 149
                         Inactive Programs 150
                         Institutions Not Responding . . . 152
                         American Studies Outside the
                             Colleges 153

CHAPTER THREE   THE AMERICAN STUDIES MOVEMENT:
                      A SUMMARY AND ANALYSIS 155

                      History and Extent 156

                      Administration 163

                      Undergraduate Programs 169

                      Undergraduate Courses 180

                      Graduate Programs 188

                      Graduate Courses 193

                      Conclusion 195

                      Bibliography 201

INDEX 203

24705

American Studies in the United States

CHAPTER ONE

A History of the Survey

The accumulation and compilation of the materials which follow has been a lengthy and laborious process involving many hands. Proper credit can be given only by a brief history of this process -- a history which will also serve to make clear the methods and criteria employed.

Sponsorship of this project has rested, from start to finish, with the American Studies Association. In the spring of 1954 Robert E. Spiller (University of Pennsylvania), then president of the ASA, appointed a Committee on American Studies Programs under the chairmanship of Edward F. Grier (University of Kansas), the purpose of which was to survey American studies activity at colleges and universities both in the United States and abroad (the scope of the survey was subsequently narrowed to the United States only). The original membership of this Committee included Bernard Bowron (University of Minnesota), William Jordy (Brown University), William Randel (Florida State University), Basil Rauch (Barnard College of Columbia University), and James Woodress (Butler University). This group, with the help of George Rogers Taylor (Amherst College), developed a questionnaire in two parts: ten pages covering administration and undergraduate activity; seven pages covering graduate activity. To determine where these questionnaires should be sent, a preliminary post-card was mailed to 841 institutions (listed in the Education Directory, Part 3, published by the U. S. Department of Health, Education, and Welfare, Office of Education for the year 1953-54). All institutions addressed were accredited by a regional organization and were not primarily technical or professional. To this preliminary mailing, made in the winter of 1954-55, 538 institutions responded, of which 178 reported some activity in American studies. In June, 1955, questionnaires were mailed to these institutions; and in

October, 1955, a list of 91 institutions with verified activity in American studies was published in American Studies.

This first major step in the survey was accomplished with the aid of the facilities of the University of Kansas and with a grant from the ASA which helped cover the costs of production and mailing of questionnaires. Since the discrepancy between the 178 affirmative responses to the post-card mailing and the 91 "verified" courses and programs may seem puzzling, this may be a good point at which to point out that the survey has sought, from start to finish, to include only activities which gave evidence of the coherent and constructive arrangement of materials, whether in courses or programs, so as to shed light on American civilization in an interdisciplinary manner. No judgment has been passed, in this process, on the value of courses or programs -- merely on the extent to which they represent serious approaches to the problem of interdisciplinary study in the American area. Doubtless some activities have been included which should not have been; even more apparently, many pertinent activities have been omitted. But the effort has been toward producing a reliable list without concern as to its size.

In the fall of 1956, Edward Grier resigned his chairmanship and a new Committee was appointed by the current president of the ASA, George Rogers Taylor. This augmented group then undertook the process of verifying the materials already on hand and putting them into usable form. For this purpose, the United States was divided in ten districts, each of which contained approximately equal activity in American Studies. Each member of the new Committee took responsibility for one of these areas; the assignments were as follows:

Committee Member	Territorial Responsibility
Robert F. Campbell (Clark University)	Connecticut, Rhode Island, Massachusetts
George Hage (University of Minnesota)	Iowa, North and South Dakota, Michigan, Minnesota, Wisconsin
John A. Hague (Stetson University)	Alabama, Florida, Georgia, Louisiana, Mississippi, Texas
Jerzy Hauptmann (Park College)	Arkansas, Illinois, Indiana, Missouri, Oklahoma
Murray Murphey (University of Pennsylvania)	Delaware, Ohio, Pennsylvania, West Virginia

James H. Stone (San Francisco State College)	California, Idaho, Nevada, Oregon, Washington
Robert H. Walker (University of Wyoming)	Arizona, Colorado, Kansas, Montana, Nebraska, New Mexico, Utah, Wyoming
John W. Ward (Princeton University)	New Jersey, New York City
Wilcomb E. Washburn (Institute of Early American History and Culture)	District of Columbia, Kentucky, Maryland, North and South Carolina, Tennessee, Virginia
William B. Whiteside (Bowdoin College)	Maine, New Hampshire, New York (other than New York City), Vermont

Checking against the returns on hand and attempting to discover newly instituted offerings where they existed, this group verified the original questionnaires and sent out new ones where necessary. On the basis of these questionnaires, and with the additional help of correspondence, phone calls, and visits in some cases, descriptive essays covering the American studies activity at each institution were written. This investigation took place from November, 1956, through January, 1958. Once the questionnaires had been checked and the descriptive essays written and returned to the institution for approval, all materials were then forwarded to the chairman. Essays were edited and made to conform to a standard format; they appear as the directory entries in the pages that follow. Thus, while the credit for compiling the information and checking for coverage in a particular area belongs clearly to the men who have been named above, the chairman must take final responsibility both for total coverage and for conclusions made in the directory descriptions. Most of the directory entries have been published substantially in the form arrived at by the individual committee members; alterations have been made for the sake of uniformity and in order to underline certain aspects of individual activities which seemed, from an over-all point of view, worthy of comment. First hand knowledge of the offerings was, regretably, lacking in too many cases; it can only be hoped that no serious inaccuracies or injustices have been committed.

Questionnaires, once completed, checked, and returned to the chairman, were coded for transmission to IBM punch cards. Using this electronic system, results were tabulated and form the basis for the statistics cited in Chapter III.

Expenses of committee members in performing their parts in the survey were contributed to by a grant from the ASA. Credit must also be given to the University of Wyoming which furnished many facilities, including the use of its IBM equipment, toward this end. The greatest debt for the completion of this stage of the survey lies with the individuals at the various institutions under survey who so patiently filled out the lengthy questionnaires, checked essays, and otherwise cooperated so helpfully with the Committee members.

Meanwhile, the Committee was also taking part in another activity which was to contribute to the present volume. The idea of a conference on undergraduate American studies courses and programs participated in by those active in these areas had first been broached by Tremaine McDowell. Negotiations with the Carnegie Corporation toward this end were carried on by Robert Spiller and by George Rogers Taylor, successive presidents of the ASA, and were concluded by Mr. Taylor. A generous grant was obtained and plans were laid by Mr. Taylor, Hennig Cohen (Executive Secretary, ASA), and the chairman for a conference to be held in Washington, D. C., March 29-31, 1957. With the membership of the Committee as a nucleus, participants were chosen on the basis of their active participation in undergraduate American studies programs. After an opening session devoted to aims and objectives, the remainder of the conference was devoted entirely to a consideration of undergraduate courses and programs. Those present at this Washington Conference were: Robert F. Campbell, Hennig Cohen, Wallace E. Davies (University of Pennsylvania), Anthony N. B. Garvan (University of Pennsylvania), John A. Hague, Jerzy Hauptmann, William Jordy, Alexander C. Kern (State University of Iowa), Murray Murphey, David M. Potter (Yale University), Robert E. Spiller, James H. Stone, George R. Taylor, Robert H. Walker, John W. Ward, Wilcomb E. Washburn, Robert H. L. Wheeler (Yale University), and William B. Whiteside. Opinions expressed at this Conference have been incorporated into Chapter III of this work in an attempt to emphasize certain points and to increase the evaluative worth of the summary. In preserving what was said there, I am particularly indebted to those who served as recorders for the five sessions, Mssrs. Davies, Hague, Jordy, Murphey, and Ward. The general feeling was that the discussion made possible by this Conference was most rewarding. If unanimity of opinion on all subjects was not attained, at least there was considerable and heartening agreement as to the importance of the work at hand and as to the major issues which would determine the success or failure of American studies.

The main ingredients of this report, then, were three: the descriptive essays pertaining to the various institutions and prepared by the individual committee members; the questionnaires and the statistics drawn from them; and the opinions expressed at the Conference in Washington, D. C. In collecting and assembling all this material, I was completely dependent on the members of my Committee and on the recorders at the Washington Conference. I would like publicly to thank these two overlapping groups for their help and to point out the large share in this report which is theirs. I am also anxious to acknowledge my debts to George Rogers Taylor and to Hennig Cohen. Mr. Taylor gave me my chance to work with these materials and furnished me with solid advice and help all the way. Mr. Cohen not only smoothed out ways and means (for Conference and survey alike), but also encouraged and advised most helpfully from start to finish. May I thank those who read all or part of the manuscript for me and whose reactions were most helpful. This group includes the recorders at the Washington Conference, and Hennig Cohen, Edward F. Grier, David M. Potter, Robert E. Spiller, George R. Taylor, and Willard Thorp. My thanks also to Donald R. Ellegood, Director of the Louisiana State University Press, for his help in bringing this work to publication so promptly.

Special attention should be called to the encouragement furnished this project by the Carnegie Corporation. As already mentioned, this organization directly sponsored the Washington Conference; furthermore, both directly and through its support of the American Studies Association, the Carnegie Corporation contributed to the progress of the survey on more than one occasion. It is no exaggeration to say that without this support this report would not have appeared.

Before my participation in this survey and in the Washington Conference, I was one of those who put quotation marks around the American Studies "movement," when I had occasion to write of it. This experience has shown me that these marks are no longer necessary, not simply because there are over a hundred American colleges and universities doing something serious in this field, but more accurately because there is enough in common at these institutions and in the minds of the men who offer American studies courses and programs to define a movement, or a central idea, rather clearly. This does not mean, in my mind, that American studies has arrived, that it has succeeded. It only means that there is now enough experience with courses, curricula, scholarship in the area of American civilization so that we know, at least, what we are trying to do. We realize our successes and our failures; we are aware of our strong and weak points. We have not, and no one feels this, found the answer. But we have by now at least achieved a sure sense of direction in our search for it.

CHAPTER TWO

A Survey of American

Studies Activities

In the directory to American studies activities which follows, colleges and universities are listed alphabetically by their formal title, all words in normal order. The index provides a more logical alphabetizing. The headings may be explained as follows:

First line: NAME OF INSTITUTION, and location.

Second line: Name of person reporting on American studies activity; his administrative position or departmental affiliation.

Third line: Extent and nature of American studies activity.

Fourth line: Date program established, or course first offered.

Fifth line: Number of majors enrolled in American studies programs as of, generally, 1957. No attempt has been made to provide course enrollments.

* before the first line indicates that data on the institution in question were received too late to be included in the tabulations on which the summary chapter was based. Institutions so marked should, therefore, be considered in addition to all totals presented in Chapter III.

Since a revised American studies directory may be attempted at a future date, it would be greatly appreciated if corrections or additions to the material which follows could be reported to the headquarters of the American Studies Association, Box 46, College Hall, University of Pennsylvania, Philadelphia 4, Pennsylvania.

* * *

A DIRECTORY TO AMERICAN STUDIES COURSES
AND PROGRAMS IN COLLEGES AND UNIVERSITIES

ADELPHI COLLEGE, Garden City, Long Island, New York.

Donald N. Koster (English), Chairman of Committee on American Civilization.

A major program of study, with course, leading to the B. A. degree in the college; there is also an evening division in which there is available a course of study, including a special course, leading to a Bachelor of Science in General Studies with a concentration in American Studies.

1953.

35 (evening); 3 (day).

ADMINISTRATION: The Program has quasi-departmental status under a chairman and a steering committee appointed as representatives of their respective fields of learning.

UNDERGRADUATE PROGRAM: Concentration in one traditional department, generally history or literature, as well as distribution across several additional departments constitutes the major pattern. The student takes a planned curriculum which culminates in the senior seminar in American civilization. In freshman and sophomore years the student takes two semesters of American national and state government, two semesters of American literature, two semesters of American history, two semesters of the history of philosophy, two years of general science, two years of foreign languages, one semester introduction to arts, one semester introduction to sociology, and a sophomore seminar in bibliography. In the junior and senior years, the student takes two semesters of American literature (seminars), two semesters of American history; two semesters of social and intellectual contact between U. S. and Europe, two semesters of American economics, one semester of modern European art, one semester American art, one semester American philosophy, and a two semester senior seminar in American civilization.

After the program had been established in the College, it was introduced into the Evening Division in a similar form. The large enrollment in this major is due to the fact that only two fields of concentration are permitted in the Evening Division -- one in science and the other in American studies.

UNDERGRADUATE COURSE: A senior seminar in American civilization selects a particular problem in American civilization for intensive study, each member doing research throughout his final two years and producing a thorough paper on a specific facet of the general problem (e. g. , the problem of slavery was the seminar topic for 1956-57). Professors of history, philosophy, and literature conduct the seminar jointly.

The sophomore course in bibliography centers on American civilization materials and represents an unique attempt to acquaint the undergraduate with the literature of this field.

COMMENT: An interdepartmental program, American civilization at Adelphi is organized around a core of learning in literature, history, and philosophy. Because an effort is made to base the program on a solid foundation of the history of human thought through the ages and of comparison of American with other civilizations, emphasis is placed on American civilization in its relationship to the rest of the world rather than upon a narrow study of our national culture. The program attempts to assure the student a coordinated pattern of study that will prepare him to meet with reasonable competence the demands made upon the responsible citizen in our society. He should be equipped to go in to graduate study or into such spheres of activity as government, business, journalism, and teaching.

ALLEGHENY COLLEGE, Meadville, Pennsylvania.

Paul A. Knights (history).

Major program leading to B. A. sponsored by history department.

1954.

3 majors.

ADMINISTRATION: The program is administered by the chairman and the staff of the department of history, which department was originally responsible for the formation of the program. The idea of an independent department is considered valid, but not expedient. The program is really interdepartmental in its offerings, but students are enrolled as history majors and the department of history takes full responsibility for the program.

UNDERGRADUATE PROGRAM: The undergraduate program requires between forty and forty-four hours work (the average major requires only thirty). The courses are those of traditional departments, including art, English, history, political science, philosophy, sociology, and economics; there is no American civilization course as such. There is, however, an individual research project carried out by the student major during his senior year, and should the enrollment be sufficient, a senior seminar is planned.

UNDERGRADUATE COURSE: In place of an upper class integrating course, senior majors in American civilization are aided in this direction by close individually supervised work in the hope that the "program may offer an integrated understanding of the full scope of American civilization, with emphasis on its historical development."

COMMENT: Allegheny already has a strong general education program so that the liberal education aspect of American civilization is probably not particularly important. Its primary interest appears to be the opportunity to study the culture of a particular geographical area; thus although there is no "culture course" either now or projected, nevertheless, the Allegheny program would seem made to order for such a plan. The program is too new to make any very meaningful evaluation; the enrollment of majors is small but it evidently has strong support from other departments.

AMHERST COLLEGE, Amherst, Massachusetts.

George R. Taylor, Chairman, American Studies Department.

A major in American Studies leading to the A. B. degree and including three courses in American Studies.

1938.

24 majors in American Studies.

ADMINISTRATION: The program is under the direction of the Chairman of an American Studies Department which has its own budget, staff and curriculum.

UNDERGRADUATE PROGRAM: At Amherst, the undergraduate major consists of an interdepartmental program of courses in history, political science, economics, philosophy and English. The course, Problems in American Civilization, is required of all sophomores regardless of their proposed major fields. Juniors and seniors majoring in American studies have a wide choice of courses but must take at least two semester courses from the American literature-philosophy group and two from the social science-history group. A good deal of emphasis is placed on the Honors Program in American Studies, and over half the majors are enrolled in this program. These students are required to take a one semester honors seminar in their junior year and two semester seminars in their senior year. Majors not taking honors are required to take a special seminar for one semester in American studies during their senior year. Measured in terms of popularity, the major is clearly successful. It ranks among the first five majors in terms of enrollment and this enrollment has been gradually increasing, perhaps because of the excellent quality of teaching in the major courses.

UNDERGRADUATE COURSES: As noted above, the introductory course called Problems in American Civilization is required of all sophomores and serves as the introductory course in American Studies. This course deals with twelve topics or problems of which six or seven are specifically historical in character. The other topics deal with current issues. The course combines large lectures with small seminar groups and uses problem materials of a character indicated by the list of titles in Amherst College, Problems in American Civilization (D. C. Heath and Co.). After listening to lectures and reading the assigned materials which present several points of view on a controversial subject, the students prepare brief papers which are the basis for the discussion groups. The Senior Seminar in American Civilization, a required course for Honors candidates in American studies, is a small seminar led by three teachers and dealing with two to four general themes or problems the contents of which shift from year to year and cover a wide range of subject matter in the area of American civilization.

GRADUATE PROGRAM: Although there is no graduate program nor department as such, the M. A. degree in American studies is very occasionally granted.

COMMENT: The Amherst program was one of the first undergraduate major programs in American studies as such. Its sophomore course in Problems in American Civilization, which also serves as a general education course in the social studies for all undergraduates, is perhaps the outstanding and unique element in this program. The problems series mentioned above, it should be noted, grew out of this course and has furnished one of the most useful and widely used set of teaching materials associated with the American studies movement. This course,

and the program as a whole, aside from the literature-philosophy requirement, is directed heavily towards the history-economics-social
science side of the picture, and therefore away from the literature and
fine arts emphasis. In the words of George R. Taylor, "the essential
purposes of this course are: first, to lead the student to become interested in and to think about the problems of modern society; and, second
to encourage him to form relevant and conscious judgments as to issues
and policies." At the same time, an effort is made in senior seminars
in American studies to get the student to interpret and integrate various
factors of American culture.

ARIZONA STATE COLLEGE, Flagstaff, Arizona.

Charles W. Meister, Director, American Civilization Program.

An American Civilization Program leading to a bachelor's degree is offered; one course is given in American Civilization which may be
taken by either undergraduate or graduate students.

1950.

2 candidates for the bachelor's degree.

ADMINISTRATION: The American civilization program at Flagstaff is a one-man operation. The program was initiated by Professor
Meister, of the English department, and he continues to administer it
without the aid of committee, maintaining a quasi-departmental status
without budget but with control of curriculum. His opinion is that departmental status would be valid but inexpedient.

UNDERGRADUATE PROGRAM: The pattern of the American studies major is interdepartmental, involving required courses in geography and history (during the first two years), and in commerce, education, sociology, history, and literature (during the final two years). To
judge by both requirements and student interest, the program focuses
on literature, first, and social science, second. An unusual aspect of
the program is that each student completing an American civilization
major must present for display in the town or at the college an interdepartmental project.

UNDERGRADUATE COURSE: Under the title "Interdivisional Studies," a course has been added to the curriculum for the benefit of

American civilization majors as well as an elective for the College at large. Staffed by an English professor, the course utilizes <u>Backgrounds</u> <u>of American Literary Thought</u>, by Horton and Edwards, as <u>the principal</u> text, and the <u>Problems in American Civilization</u> series published by Amherst College as the main sources of collateral readings. Including materials from all the major disciplines, this course is organized topically as follows: Religious and Moral Currents; Political, Economic, and Social Currents; Literary, Artistic, and Musical Currents; Philosophic and Educational Currents; and Current Problems in American Civilization. The method includes lectures, student reports, and class discussion. Enrollment for the course is provided mainly by practising or prospective elementary school teachers who find it useful as a supplement to the liberal education curriculum and as preparation for teaching in core curricula.

GRADUATE COURSE: The course described above is offered as both undergraduate and graduate elective.

COMMENT: The program provides a variety of approaches to the study of American civilization with the aim of deepening "the student's understanding and appreciation of the growth of American ideals, institutions and thought, " to quote the catalogue entry. The program itself has attracted but a very small enrollment, and the faculty attitude toward the program is described as indifferent. An apparent weakness of the program consists in its failure to provide sufficient emphasis on civilizations other than the American for purposes of showing comparisons and historical development.

The interdivisional course, which is the only specific offering under the program, has apparently enjoyed a wide success and popularity. The Director feels that the American civilization program is well adapted to the training not only of future teachers and businessmen (which represents the present focus), but also of future ministers, social workers, and news commentators.

ARKANSAS POLYTECHNIC COLLEGE, Russellville, Arkansas.

T. R. Garrison (English).

An American civilization course only (on the undergraduate level).

1954.

Course required on the sophomore level with 150-175 enrollment.

ADMINISTRATION: A steering committee made up of representatives from the departments of English and history is appointed by the Dean. The members elect their chairman. The representative of the English department spends about 2/3 of his teaching time in the course, the representative of the history department about 2/3. The program was supported by the Ford Foundation until 1956, and since that time has been maintained by the college.

UNDERGRADUATE COURSE: The course is entitled "Our American Heritage" and is a required course on the sophomore level. It is taught by the members of the departments mentioned above and contains material from these two fields, as well as from philosophy. The course is organized around a chronological-historical core with other disciplines dovetailed in as the nation's history unfolds. Lectures are delivered by the specialists from the participating fields supplemented by small (maximum 25 students) discussion sections led by the lecturers. Standard textbooks in the field of American history and literature are used.

COMMENT: The course is required as a part of the general education core, but is surprisingly popular for a required course. The attitude of the faculty toward it is generally favorable, although some opposition is also evident. The importance of this course lies in the fact that it is designed as a general education course for students who receive a technical education. Beginning as a broad experimental course including the fine arts as well as history and literature, the course was forced to contract its scope due to a committee ruling which pointed out overlapping in the fine arts subject matter. In spite of this and in spite of some reported staff shortages, this course apparently continues to function as a central part of the student's experience.

AUGUSTANA COLLEGE, Rock Island, Illinois.

O. Fritiof Ander (history), Director of American Studies.

An American Studies Program leading to the B. A., and including one course in American Civilization.

1946.

3 majors.

ADMINISTRATION: The program is a cooperative effort of several departments: Christianity, economics, English, geography, history, philosophy, political science and sociology. A steering committee made up of the chairmen of the departments of English and history directs the program. No thought is given to the creation of a special American studies department.

UNDERGRADUATE PROGRAM: The requirements for an American studies major include the following courses: two semesters American history, one semester European history, two semesters American literature, two semesters history of the West, one semester of American government, one semester of a course in "The Growth of American Ideals," one semester American church history, and one semester of either labor problems or "European Background of American People." In addition to this central group of courses the student takes advanced work in either American literature (14 semester hours), or the social sciences (12 semester hours). In each case this work includes a seminar in history or in literature. The program is meant for especially good students and appeals mainly to those who intend to enter into diplomatic service or who wish to become journalists.

UNDERGRADUATE COURSE: Courses titled "American Studies Seminar" are offered to advanced students in both literature and history; they do not presuppose any dedication to the American studies approach, however, but merely allow directed research in many directions. The presence of the American studies program has fostered the addition, under the auspices of the history department, of a new American civilization course. Based on readings in R. H. Gabriel and Perry Miller and titled "The Growth of American Ideals," this course includes materials from the fields of economics, history, literature, philosophy, political science, religion, and sociology in its focus on American ideals from 1815 to the present. This course is required of all American studies majors and has proved popular as an elective on the upper class level.

COMMENT: This program is a rather complex elaboration of "the Augustana method" and was especially influenced by World War II area studies. On account of its complexity and hour load, the program has attracted very few students; it has, however, reportedly served its purpose of providing the exceptional student an insight into American life and history not available through a customary departmental major. Within the program, careful attention to history, literature, philosophy, religion, and the social sciences has precluded any place for the fine arts or the esthetic approach. Although the program itself has not proved popular, many of the courses associated with it have.

BARNARD COLLEGE OF COLUMBIA UNIVERSITY, New York, N. Y.

Basil Rauch (history), Chairman of the Program in American Civilization.

A major program leading to the A. B. degree with three special courses in American Civilization.

1939-49; re-established 1952.

25 majors.

ADMINISTRATION: The program has non-departmental status and is administered by a steering committee (chosen purely on the basis of their interest in American civilization); there is no separate budget, but a staff and control of curriculum.

UNDERGRADUATE PROGRAM: The student is required to take two introductory and one advanced courses in the humanities and two introductory and one advanced courses in the social sciences, besides three courses specifically designed for American civilization majors. Although the program distributes its emphasis almost equally, the humanities have received slightly more student attention.

UNDERGRADUATE COURSES: In the sophomore year the student is required to take an introductory survey of the history of American civilization; this course is also open to non-majors. It is organized around special topics chronologically arranged, and features both lecture and discussion periods. The popularity of this course is about equal to that of the traditional history survey course with which it "competes." In the junior year, the student takes a reading course in American civilization which consists of a required list of basic titles and a selection among titles representing the approaches of various disciplines; open only to majors in the program, this course is conducted on the conference method and is based on extensive reading done largely in the summer proceeding the junior year. In the senior year, the student participates in a seminar built around individual research papers on a topic which varies from year to year.

COMMENT: Supported in its first five years (1952-1957) by a grant from the Carnegie Corporation, the Barnard program is carefully thought out and well organized. Barnard has also sponsored a distinguished annual series of lectures which is integrated with the students' work in the program. The purpose of the program is to allow a student to pursue her interest in the study of American civilization across the barriers of departmental specialization. Because of a highly favorable faculty attitude and a legacy of voluntary interest not found in connection with more traditional programs, those at Barnard feel that the program will have no difficulty proceeding without subsidy in the future.

BAYLOR UNIVERSITY, Waco, Texas.

E. Hudson Long (American literature).

An interdepartmental major leading to the A. B. and M. A. degrees. One special American civilization course is offered and is required of both graduate and undergraduate majors.

1950.

No undergraduate majors; 4 M. A. candidates.

ADMINISTRATION: The American studies program at Baylor offers an interdepartmental major and is co-chairmaned by the history and English departments. The program is treated as a quasi-department which establishes its own requirements for a major in American studies. Participating departments include: English, history, sociology, philosophy, political science, economics, education, and religion.

UNDERGRADUATE PROGRAM: As a major, the student must complete one course each in sociology, religion, political science, philosophy, education, and economics. He must, in addition, complete three courses in American literature and two in American history, or, three in history and two in literature. From 1950 to 1954, only two students had graduated with an A. B. in American studies.

UNDERGRADUATE COURSE: There is a special course offered for the American studies major under the general direction of the professor of American literature. It is a one-term proseminar with a major emphasis in American literature and history, although seminar papers are also prepared on education, philosophy, religion, and social science. The purpose of this seminar would appear to be that of furnishing the undergraduate major with an opportunity to demonstrate his broadened knowledge of the intellectual and cultural development of the country.

GRADUATE PROGRAM: The graduate program is of a restricted nature as only eight students have thus far participated; three have received the M. A. in American studies. It is possible for a major in history or literature to combine his work with courses in philosophy and religion, or the fine arts.

GRADUATE COURSE: Candidates for the M. A. in American Studies are also required to take the proseminar described above.

COMMENT: The program has been in operation a relatively short time and has had limited success. Its purpose is to acquaint the student with the intellectual and cultural development of the nation, to prepare him for responsible citizenship, and to show the continuity of past, present, and future in terms acceptable, both scientifically and historically. The program has been implemented by a series of public lectures on American Ideals given each spring. Speakers for this program have been Senator Symington, Secretary Anderson, and the Norwegian ambassador. The program is frankly aimed at quality students and emphasizes training for leadership.

BENNETT COLLEGE, Greensboro, North Carolina.

George Breathett, Chairman, Social Science Core Committee.

An American studies program leading to the B. A. degree.

1953.

3 candidates for the B. A.

ADMINISTRATION: The American civilization program at Bennett is administered by a steering committee within the department of social sciences appointed by the college's "Central Committee." The program was set up with the cooperation of all elements of the social sciences department. Full departmental status for the program is considered valid and expedient.

UNDERGRADUATE PROGRAM: Requirements for the undergraduate major program in American studies are identical with the general college requirements for the freshmen and sophomore years. In the junior and senior years two semesters of American government, one semester of economics, two semesters of history, two semesters of American literature, one semester of social history, and a course in "Special Problems," are required. In sum, majors are required to take courses in history, literature, philosophy, religion, political science, sociology, and economics. Although a specific grade average is required of prospective majors, standing of students in the field compared with others in the college is average. Films have been used as an extracurricular aid.

UNDERGRADUATE COURSE: Bennett College is interested in introducing special American civilization courses, but with insufficient funds it is impossible to increase personnel for this purpose.

COMMENT: The purpose of the American Studies program is to give a simple, straightforward account of the development of American civilization from the earliest times to the present. While no rigid interpretation is used, four main themes--politico-economic, social, cultural, and religious--are emphasized, and the interactions of these factors are carefully weighed. It is felt that a thorough understanding of the various facets of American civilization enables the student to form a synthesis which leads to a more intelligent citizenship and leadership in our society. Faculty attitude is favorable to the program and two new history courses have been added as a result of it.

BENNINGTON COLLEGE, Bennington, Vermont.

Rush Welter, Faculty member in American civilization.

Highly individualized undergraduate major program in American civilization including a two-year course.

1950.

Figures requested but not received.

ADMINISTRATION: The American civilization program at Bennington is under the supervision of an ad hoc committee of faculty members. The faculty member chiefly responsible for the major program was trained in American civilization specifically. Other members of the committee represent history, literature, philosophy, visual arts, and music.

The Bennington program was instituted with the aid of a Carnegie Corporation grant. At first it featured visiting participants, invited to lecture and lead discussions; the book, America in Crisis, edited by Daniel Aaron, is a compilation based upon the first year's program (1950-1951). More recently the program has relied upon a wide variety of course offerings within the college curriculum.

UNDERGRADUATE PROGRAM: Any undergraduate at Bennington is free to work out, under faculty guidance, an individualized program of study. If her major interest is American civilization she will usually have taken a year in American history and other courses or seminars in American literature and philosophy by the time she defines her major (at the end of the sophomore year). From that point on, her program includes a number of related courses which illuminate various aspects of American civilization; the culminating project is the preparation of a thesis.

UNDERGRADUATE COURSES: Among the usual major courses in junior and senior years is a two-year cycle of courses taught on a seminar basis. The first year deals with topics in the period 1828-1865, and the second year with the period 1890-1950. The second half of each year attempts for the period under consideration an "historic analysis of American thought and character." Primary sources are emphasized in the reading, with supplemental use of significant conceptual or interpretive essays by such authors as Gabriel, Mumford, Santayana, etc. These courses are given in alternate years and may be taken separately, or counter-chronologically.

COMMENT: The effort of the whole curriculum is to "produce a more thoughtful kind of college graduate than traditional curricula can." The vitality of the Bennington program in American civilization is undoubtedly due chiefly to the insistence upon keeping formal course requirements to a minimum, while devoting considerable thoughtful attention to the educational background and intellectual interests of each student. The scheme permits infinite variation from year to year and from student to student, and it seems well suited to discourage rigid formalization, to the extent even of being "not easily identifiable as a 'program' in American Civilization." Among several examples of "permissive" major programs, this one is notable for its inclusion of a two-year course cycle which must be of great aid to the student's efforts at integration of knowledge.

BROOKLYN COLLEGE, Brooklyn, New York.

John Hope Franklin (history).

One undergraduate course in American Studies.

1940.

ADMINISTRATION: The course is offered under the general auspices of the history and philosophy departments, and administered by the two professors (one from each department) who offer the course.

UNDERGRADUATE COURSE: Based mainly on primary sources in the fields of history, literature, and philosophy, the course seeks "to present a multi-dimensional picture of our culture. Its validity comes from its unique character in providing perspective and understanding of American life that is not undertaken elsewhere in the college program." This two-term course carries double credit (6 hours), meets for from four to seven hours a week, and invariably attracts more students than the limit of 15 per term allows. In addition to the regular two-man staff, visiting lecturers are called upon regularly. The method of the course might be described as a combination of the great books approach, selected topics arranged chronologically, and individual research. Supplementary readings cover major secondary and interpretive approaches to American thought.

COMMENT: Judging from the impressive list of readings, and from the over-subscribed enrollment, this course obviously succeeds in offering the senior student a useful, coordinated picture of his civilization in the area of history, literature, and philosophy.

BROWN UNIVERSITY: Providence, R. I. (includes Pembroke College).

William G. McLoughlin, Jr., Acting Chairman, American Civilization Committee (Donald H. Fleming, Chairman, on leave 1956-57).

Major in American Civilization leading to A. B. degree; graduate programs leading to M. A. and Ph. D. degrees; and special courses, graduate and undergraduate.

1945.

Undergraduate program, 64; graduate programs, M. A., 10; Ph. D., 10.

ADMINISTRATION: The American civilization program at Brown is under the supervision of a chairman and two committees representing the participating departments and having control of the curriculum. The personnel of the two committees is overlapping to some extent though the general committee is somewhat larger than the undergraduate committee. Staff and budget are under the control of the traditional departments, with the exception of budgetary provision for two teaching associates appointed by the committee.

UNDERGRADUATE PROGRAM: The undergraduate program is an interdepartmental major representing the fields of history, English, political science, economics, philosophy and art. All majors are required to take either the survey course in American history or the "History of American Economic Life"; a semester course in early colonial history; a full year course in American literature; and a semester course entitled "Problems in American Civilization." In addition, they must choose two courses from a list which includes courses in American art, philosophy, science, religion, political thought and social and intellectual history. This major ranks among the five most popular majors in the college and appears to attract students of above average intelligence and ability.

UNDERGRADUATE COURSE: As indicated above, majors in American civilization are required in their senior year to take a one-semester course entitled "Problems in American Civilization." This course varies in content from year to year, but is usually organized around some important theme such as "Foreign Influences in American Thought." While a number of teaching methods are used, emphasis is placed upon discussion groups led by two or three specialists. A second semester of the American civilization course is required of honors candidates and is devoted to the preparation of the thesis under individual supervision.

GRADUATE PROGRAM: Brown University offers both the M. A. and the Ph. D. degrees in American civilization. Candidates for the Ph. D. must prepare themselves in six fields, which must include American economic and social history, and American literature; a choice of two or three from such fields as American political thought, American philosophy, American science, American religion, such areas as European or English history, literature, and philosophy. M. A. programs are worked out on an individual basis, but are designed to include courses from several fields or disciplines. Both M. A. and Ph. D. theses, of course, have been written on subjects which cut across traditional departmental lines. All candidates for graduate degrees in American civilization must at the outset satisfy the Committee that they have a broad knowledge of European, English and American history as well as the history of philosophy. Most of the "products" of this graduate program find positions teaching in departments of history, though about one in five becomes associated with English departments. In spite of some placement difficulties, an increasing number of graduate students have chosen to enroll.

GRADUATE COURSE: All candidates for advanced degrees in American civilization must take a full year seminar in American civilization, the purpose of which is to examine a period or movement in American history from several points of view. Papers are presented by both faculty and students on a weekly basis for critical discussion. One stated aim is to produce original research with a view toward publication of the results.

COMMENT: The graduate and undergraduate programs in American civilization are designed to offer students at Brown University the opportunity to study intensively the history and culture of the United States. These programs are based on the assumption that a civilization can best be understood by examining its achievements in several different fields. The graduate program specifically recognizes the importance of relating American to European civilization. Both the graduate and the undergraduate programs include specific courses in American civilization, each of which seeks to explore some aspects of American civilization from different points of view; and the undergraduate course, especially, seeks to integrate material around a common theme. One apparent characteristic of the American civilization program is its emphasis on history (in staff, student training and interest, course offerings, placement tendencies) at the expense of other departments, notably literature.

CALIFORNIA INSTITUTE OF TECHNOLOGY, Pasadena, California.

Rodman W. Paul, Chairman of History Staff, Humanities Division.

Required sophomore course.

1948.

ADMINISTRATION: The required sophomore course in American civilization is offered by the Humanities Division of the Institute. Direction of the course is in the hands of the chairman of the history staff

of the Division, which combines all non-scientific fields. Carnegie
Corporation funds were used to help the course get underway, provide
for the strengthening of the staff, and purchase books. The staff consists of faculty members who represent and instruct, respectively, in
history, government, and English, in addition to their responsibilities
for the required American studies course. Their opportunities for professional advancement in connection with the course equal those in their
special fields. It is the chairman's view that informal staff operations,
based upon mutual interest and assistance, have been a principal basis
for the evolution and improvement of the course, and that special preparation in "American Studies" has not been of greater advantage than
competence in a special field plus open-mindedness.

UNDERGRADUATE COURSE: The course in American civilization
(a full year in duration) is organized on an historical framework to deal
with six major topics or problems: national and state government; democracy and economic opportunity in the early national period; the causes
of the Civil War; the Industrial Revolution; 20th century change and re-
sistance to change; and international responsibilities. The course stresses the interdisciplinary concept; where materials can be made to fit
into the total picture (as in English and government) they are retained,
where they cannot be assimilated (as in economics) they are discarded.
Students work from a large number of texts and source materials in history and government, some in entirety, some in part; supplementary
material is provided by mimeograph. Classes range from 15-20 students, and are carried throughout by a single instructor. Discussion,
rather than lecture, is the common mode of instruction.

COMMENT: The course is similar in many respects to the common means whereby California colleges and universities provide general
education instruction in history and government as a basis for mature
citizenship in their students. Because of the high calibre of the students
(among the top 2-3% of the nation) at the Institute, the staff has been able
to demand far more than usual in readings and, probably, in other respects of the work. More than in most such courses, it also appears,
there is a definite effort to unify several disciplines rather than merely
to place them end to end. The recent addition of literature to the historical and political content of the course, moreover, gives it a broader
approach than is typical of most required American history courses in
the State. This latest step in the development of the course also indicates that its evolution is still continuing.

CLARK UNIVERSITY, Worcester, Massachusetts.

Robert F. Campbell (history).

American civilization major leading to A. B. degree and including a
    "Senior Conference in American Civilization."

1948.

5 undergraduate majors in American civilization.

ADMINISTRATION: This program is in charge of a director who
is assisted by an advisory committee representing traditional departments; but there is wide delegation of authority to the director.

UNDERGRADUATE PROGRAM: The major consists of an interdepartmental program of courses in history, government, literature,
economics, sociology and philosophy. Majors are required in their
freshman and sophomore years to take "General Education 14--Europe
and the U. S. since 1500, " and two of the three introductory courses in
economics, government and sociology. In the junior and senior years,
majors must take American literature, U. S. social and intellectual
history, both full year courses, and a semester "Senior Conference in
American Civilization." In addition, majors must choose the equivalent
of two full year courses from a list of courses in related fields. Honors
students normally substitute three semesters of reading courses in various areas for some of the courses normally selected in related fields.
In one of these courses, they are required to prepare an honors thesis.
The major ranks only among the third five in terms of popularity, and
there does not appear to be a trend upward.

UNDERGRADUATE COURSE: This is a semester course in Amer-
ican civilization which is partially designed to assist the students in preparing for their comprehensive examinations. This course is taught by
the director with the occasional assistance of experts in special fields,
especially American literature. Using primarily materials selected
from the Amherst Series, Problems in American Civilization, this
course is essentially a seminar or discussion course based on topics
arranged chronologically, most of which have been touched upon in other
courses taken by the majors.

COMMENT: This program is one of two or three interdepartmental
majors designed to permit students who are interested in American culture to choose a series of related courses without strict regard to departmental lines. In the opinion of the director, the program needs im-

provement especially in the direction of strengthening the Senior Conference so that it will better serve an interpretive and integrating function. It would also be helpful if courses in American art and architecture were added to the college curriculum.

COLBY COLLEGE, Waterville, Maine.

David Bridgman, Chairman of American Studies major.

Major program leading to the B. A.

1955.

10 majors.

ADMINISTRATION: Operating under the sponsorship of the history department, the program is administered by a committee chaired by a member of this department and composed of members of such other departments as English, economics, and philosophy. This status accurately represents departmental initiative in inaugurating the program.

UNDERGRADUATE PROGRAM: The American studies major is designed to permit a formalized concentration in the American field not similarly possible under existing curricula. This is accomplished by a set of requirements including 6 semesters in American history, 2 semesters of American government, and 4 semesters of American literature. Other requirements, in economics, religion, philosophy, and European history, serve both to increase the student's knowledge of the American field and to aid him in putting this knowledge into perspective with societies outside the United States.

COMMENT: Although a slight increase in enrollment is anticipated for the coming year, this program is as yet so new and has been undertaken by so few students that those responsible for it are as yet disinclined to generalize concerning it. No curricular adjustments have been felt necessary, although a need is acknowledged for a senior integrating seminar to be sponsored by the history department. Aside from the putative advantages of cross-departmental study, no special claims are made for the program and no great effort is made, apparently, to recommend it to students.

COLGATE UNIVERSITY, Hamilton, New York.

Marvin Wachman (history), director of upperclass core program.

Programs leading to B. A. and M. A. degrees; special courses in American civilization required of all undergraduates.

1938 (undergraduate); 1946 (graduate).

1 candidate for the B. A. (others as yet potential); 1 candidate for the M. A.

ADMINISTRATION: Under a quasi-departmental status, a chairman coordinates the participation of representatives of the departments of history, English, philosophy and religion, political science, economics, and sociology. These representatives, all interested in the American field, administer the program; the required course has a separate organizational entity independent of existing departmental lines.

UNDERGRADUATE PROGRAM: Undergraduates majoring in American civilization have been required to complete a basic program including two semesters of American history, one semester of American literature, one semester of American government, one semester of social philosophy, and "some work in art and music." Advanced courses are selected by the individual student, in consultation with his advisor, to suit his particular needs and interests. Since the course requirements exceed those for traditional departmental majors, the American civilization major program attracts a relatively small number of students (sometimes as few as one or two from a class), and participating faculty members discourage run-of-the-mill students from electing the major. Presently the entire major is in a period of transition and is "tailored to an individual's need."

UNDERGRADUATE COURSES: All undergraduates, whatever their major, are required to take a two-semester course in the junior year in "American Ideals and Institutions." This course represents probably Colgate's most intensive sustained effort in American civilization as such. Inaugurated in 1949 as a one-semester senior course, it proved highly successful and was expanded into a year course in 1956. Participating instructors use a common syllabus, but add supplementary reading assignments which they vary according to the background of the students. Thus a science major, for example, would have to do a considerable amount of basic reading, whereas a history or American civilization major would be directed toward more advanced reading to supplement his other work at Colgate. The heart of the course is in small classes, each taught by one of the participating instructors. There are a few lectures each semester by outside authorities in various fields. Reading assignments are in source documents, problem reading, etc., many of which are prepared by the staff in mimeographed form.

The course is part of a required upperclass sequence which places American civilization in its world context. This sequence includes the study of a foreign area and a one-semester course in "America in the World Community," taken in the senior year. This course presents a combined program of classes, readings, and independent study designed to develop in the student a "decision-maker's approach" to international problems and foreign policy. At the end of the semester each student presents before the class a report in which specific foreign policy proposals are made and defended. (See Marvin Wachman, "Colgate's Course in the American Idea," Journal of Higher Education XXVI [May, 1955], 242-49).

GRADUATE PROGRAM: Terminating with the M. A., Colgate's graduate program has always had a small enrollment and has never developed a fixed pattern of requirements. Students are directed to a curriculum based on their background and future needs. (The sole special requirement involves an interdisciplinary thesis.). They come equally from history, literature, and political science; half of them continue to the doctorate elsewhere; others use their training in secondary teaching. The student adviser feels that graduate students should have a strong training in a traditional subject in order to increase job opportunities.

COMMENT: The senior course is obviously the strong point of American civilization activity at Colgate; in fact, those connected with the program regard it yet as but a more or less formless collection of separate courses and not especially worth the extra course load involved. Furthermore, special demands on the undergraduates for course time have made any extra-load programs of doubtful efficacy. Until an integrated program can be developed (including interdisciplinary seminars for both undergraduates and graduates), the faculty will hesitate to recommend American civilization to its students.

COLLEGE OF ST. CATHERINE, St. Paul, Minnesota.

Sister Teresa, chairman of the history department and acting director of American studies.

An American studies program leading to the B. A., including a course in American studies.

1955.

7 candidates for the B. A.

ADMINISTRATION: The American studies program at St. Catherine's is directed by a member of the history department, in consultation with an informal committee representing departments offering relevant courses. A number of departments were active in instituting the program's offerings: history, literature, philosophy, speech and drama, music, sociology, psychology, political science, and economics. In the opinion of the director, departmental status would be valid, except that the college is not large enough to warrant it.

UNDERGRADUATE PROGRAM: Requirements for the B. A. in American studies are all upper division courses: at least two semesters of history of the United States, at least one semester each of government of the United States, American literature, and "American Ideas and Value Concepts"; one semester of American music or of American art history; and a two-semester seminar in American studies. Majors must also comply with the college's general requirements of a course in world literature, history of Europe to 1648, and two years of a foreign language. The program, then, is best described as an interdepartmental major including humanities, social sciences, and history. A C-plus average is required for admission to the program, and students are above the college average in intellectual ability. A number of courses have been added to the offerings of traditional departments as a result of the program. These include: "The Far West in American History," "American Folklore," "American Music," "History of American Art," "American Ideas and Value Concepts," and the integrating seminar course described below.

UNDERGRADUATE COURSE: The integrating seminar in American studies is taken in the senior year. It is organized around a single theme by a different instructor each term. Lectures are given both by the director for the semester and by other faculty members invited by the director. At least one of the two periods each week is devoted to discussion. Disciplines drawn on in the development of the themes include art, architecture, history, literature, music, philosophy, and religion.

COMMENT: The aims of the program are summarized under four headings: to understand the origins, special character, and values of American culture; to appreciate the American heritage as revealed in the history and political institutions, the art and literature, and the ideals and tested convictions of the American people; to develop the power of integrating materials gathered from working in several separate disciplines; and to offer opportunity for creative and sustained thinking in an area not covered by any single text or reference. The program has elicited a very favorable reaction from the faculty generally and enthusiastic support from the administration.

COLUMBIA UNIVERSITY, New York 27, New York.

Robert Cumming, (philosophy).

One course in the School of General Studies: open to juniors, seniors, and graduate students.

1952.

10-15 (approx.).

ADMINISTRATION: The course in American civilization is offered in the School of General Studies under no special departmental auspices, but staffed by faculty trained in philosophy and literature.

UNDERGRADUATE COURSE: "American Civilization 1-2" in the School of General Studies is built around special topics arranged chronologically and taught by the discussion method. The course is mainly concerned with the growth of those ideas and institutions which help to explain contemporary American civilization. Emphasis is placed at the outset on comparative studies of civilization followed by extensive readings focusing broadly on various ideological concepts and conflicts central to the development of American civilization.

COMMENT: This course represents an ambitious effort to provide the broadest sort of contact with the ideas elemental to an understanding of our society. Its motive was to attract students interested in a general education. What popularity the course achieved was in spite of voluminous reading assignments. Recently it has been decided that this course is failing to attract the type of students for which it was intended; a decision is being considered which would modify the course and direct it toward the needs of foreign students.

CORNELL UNIVERSITY, Ithaca, New York.

Robert H. Elias (English), Chairman, Committee on American Studies.

Program leading to the B. A. including special senior seminar. See also
   below under "Graduate Program."

1950.

20 candidates for the B. A.

ADMINISTRATION: Representatives of the American field from various departments make up the administrative authority for the American studies major; the course in American civilization, however, is not a responsibility of this committee but of the individual teaching it.

UNDERGRADUATE PROGRAM: The undergraduate major program requires the following courses in American studies fields: (a) two semesters of American literature, two semesters of American history, one semester of American philosophy; (b) two additional semesters in a "sequence of social science study devoted to the United States, chosen from the field of economics, government, or sociology"; (c) four semesters of advanced course work within one single discipline; and (d) a two-semester American studies senior seminar. In addition, the student must take four semesters of supplementary background work in European culture. The concentration by American studies majors under (b) and (c) above has been mostly in history and government for the past two years.

UNDERGRADUATE COURSE: The senior seminar in American civilization is open only to majors in this field and is required of them. All characteristics of this course have varied so from term to term that it is impossible to generalize concerning it. The staff has included members of several departments, but especially English and history; the theme has varied from the consideration of a single decade to the consideration of the assumptions of various disciplines.

GRADUATE PROGRAM: Although Cornell grants no advanced degree in American studies, it is worth noting that graduate requirements are sufficiently flexible to allow for what amounts to an American civilization curriculum within many of the traditional departments, especially history. Many students have undertaken such a program; but because of the satisfactoriness of the present arrangement, and because it is felt that graduate students will have better job opportunities if they take up a traditional program, there is no pressure to adopt a graduate program in American studies.

COMMENT: The American studies program at Cornell offers unusually rich opportunities for the selection of courses in the various fields related to American studies. The senior seminar, combined with advisory guidance throughout the major program, offers a means for the integration of the departmental courses. The tendency of some students to elect American studies because it enables them to dip into several fields without intensive study in any one suggests, however, that a more complete integration would be desirable.' This is obviously true of graduate work in American studies as well. An overemphasis upon social studies was noted in the early stage of the program, but this has been considerably reduced.

DOUGLASS COLLEGE OF RUTGERS UNIVERSITY (formerly New Jersey College for Women), New Brunswick, New Jersey.

George P. Schmidt, (history).

An interdepartmental major leading to an A. B. in American studies.

1944.

2 majors.

ADMINISTRATION: Two departmental chairmen (English and history) act as advisers to those students desiring to put together an interdepartmental major in the field of American studies.

UNDERGRADUATE PROGRAM: In addition to the requirements for all liberal arts majors in the college, students take American history and American literature in their sophomore year, plus a pattern of no less than four American courses designed to meet the needs of the individual student. Otherwise, there is no special course or program in American studies.

COMMENT: For Douglass College, American civilization is one of a number of majors which cross departmental lines (such as Latin-American Studies, International Relations) and is designed to allow a student interested in focusing on a concept or on an area of study in American life to do so. Although this program is by definition a loose one, samples of fields of concentration developed by American studies majors under the direction of their advisors show that sensible and usable courses of study are consistently recommended. Combinations have been made of intellectual history, philosophy, and religion, for example, or of the history of literature and the fine arts in America.

EASTERN NEW MEXICO UNIVERSITY, Portales, New Mexico.

B. June West, (English).

Undergraduate course.

1950.

UNDERGRADUATE PROGRAM: No American studies program exists at present, but considerable interest has been developing and the formulation of a program may be anticipated at some future time.

UNDERGRADUATE COURSE: The course titled "Main Currents in American Thought," is open to juniors, seniors, and first year graduate students as an elective, and is offered for either English or history credit. It is taught by a member of the English department with the aid of occasional outside lectures. The content of the course is described as social-intellectual history combined with a modified great books approach. Looking Backward, Progress and Poverty, and other such works are subjected to thorough examination via the methods of lecture, discussion, and special report. Materials from the several disciplines are utilized with the object of surveying the principal aspects of American cultural history from 1607 to the present. The course attracts better than average students and has enjoyed a marked popularity. Typical enrollment is twenty students per term.

FLORIDA STATE UNIVERSITY, Tallahassee, Florida.

William Randel, Director of American Studies.

Programs leading to both A. B. and M. A. degrees including a special course required of both graduate and undergraduate majors.

1948.

7 candidates for the A. B.; one candidate for the M. A.

ADMINISTRATION: The program at Florida State is administered under a director, as an interdepartmental program without budget. The director feels that both the lack of a budget and his own absence from the program for two different years have inhibited maximum efficacy of direction.

UNDERGRADUATE PROGRAM: Students who major in American studies must have completed the general education requirements of the University which include courses in history, social studies, humanities; the major must take the required American civilization course and must otherwise distribute his course work among the four following areas: literature; history; philosophy, music, and art; and social studies. There is also a foreign language-civilization requirement. As the reputation of the program has spread, enrollment has increased up to a high point of 13 majors in 1954 plus several equivalent majors.

UNDERGRADUATE COURSE: A two-semester seminar, offered by the director, is required of all majors. The first term is dedicated to a review of various theories of American civilization, under which headings are integrated the diverse course experiences of the students. During the second term, a broad common topic is chosen (such as "Is there an American Civilization?") on which guests speakers -- or groups of guest speakers -- address the class and help lead discussions thereafter. This second-term program has proved popular not only as an elective course but also as a non-credit lecture-discussion series of interest to members of the community.

GRADUATE PROGRAM: The graduate Program has not developed satisfactorily; only two students have thus far completed the M. A. Graduate students are expected to work in three of the four areas described above; graduate work in American studies is also available as an informal minor to candidates for traditional degrees.

GRADUATE COURSE: Candidates for the M. A. in American studies are required to take the course described above.

COMMENT: In spite of the fact that American studies has had no great numerical success, it has already left its mark on the institution and is recognized as the most successful of the interdisciplinary efforts made there. The program arose out of a need for a broadened liberal education resulting from the restricted nature of some of the traditional offerings. Already, as a result of efforts made in connection with this program, courses have been added in the departments of history ("The Intellectual History of the U. S."), English ("Contemporary Trends"), and the social sciences. The unique and valuable relationships with the community made possible through the special American civilization course should also be noted.

Milligan College Library
Milligan College, Tennessee

FORDHAM UNIVERSITY, New York 58, New York.

J. R. Frese, Director.

An interdepartmental major leading to a B. A. or a B. S. (Bachelor in Social Science); three undergraduate courses.

1950.

25 majors.

ADMINISTRATION: The program is directed by a committee of the heads of the cooperating departments (communication arts, English, history, philosophy, political philosophy and the social sciences) with a Director responsible directly to the dean of the college. Another faculty member serves as Administrative Assistant and gives seventy-five percent of his time to the program. The program exists in quasi-departmental status since it has control of its own curriculum. An interesting feature of the administrative organization of the Fordham program is that it was originally organized as a department and gradually moved toward its present structure; it is felt that departmental status was simply an expedient in order to put the program on its feet but not valid as a permanent status.

UNDERGRADUATE PROGRAM: For admission to the program the student must satisfy the committee of his preparedness in the field of American history either through course work or independent readings. Three courses, a two-term course in junior year and two one-term courses in senior year, are required of all majors in the program; these are special courses in American civilization and comprise one-half of the student's required course work toward a degree. The other half consists of a selection of courses (under the supervision of the committee) from any two of the six participating departments (see above). In addition to course requirements, the student must present special written reports and pass an oral examination in American civilization.

UNDERGRADUATE COURSES: "American Civilization 31-32" is a two-term junior course which aims to be a coordinating survey and introduction to the study of American civilization through an analysis of the American scene--its society and institutions, its culture and thought -- drawing upon sources in classical and Christian traditions and stressing the influence these sources have continued to bear on the development of America. Emphasis in lectures, materials, and assigned reports rests on the inter-relations of various specific fields of study. "American Civilization 33, " the American Renaissance, is a study of major literary artists in mid-nineteenth century America. "American Civilization 34," a seminar in the spring term of senior year, is based upon special projects of the students which have been in preparation, under committee supervision, since the junior year.

COMMENT: This program aims to satisfy the needs of students who wish to obtain a broad and basic understanding of the development and culture of the United States. It is designed as a terminal course, and students planning to do advanced work are urged to enter a traditional department; graduates generally enter law, business, teaching or journalism. Originally limited to fifteen students a year, demand (as many as forty applications per year) has pushed the limit up to twenty-five. This number (40) compares with any other major in Fordham College. The program has seemed to attract not only students of above average intelligence (due to the extra work load and competitive selectivity) but also of above average leaderships qualities, to judge by various campus criteria. Although established administratively, the program has attained through its excellence a degree of popularity with faculty as well as with students and administrators.

GEORGETOWN UNIVERSITY, Washington, D. C.

Rev. Joseph A. Sellinger, S. J., Associate Dean of the College.

An American civilization major program leading to the A. B. degree.

1952.

No enrollment data available.

ADMINISTRATION: The American civilization program is administered within the history and government department and directed by the chairman and staff of that department.

UNDERGRADUATE PROGRAM: Prerequisites for the major in American civilization consist of courses in American history and American government in the freshman and sophomore years. In the junior and senior years of the major two semesters of American literature, two semesters of American government, and two semesters of American history are taken. Majors are required to complete courses in the following fields: history, literature, philosophy, religion, and foreign civilization.

COMMENT: Aside from a brief mention in the catalogue, evidence of the existence of this program has been hard to accumulate. There is, evidently, an American civilization major as described above; but, apparently, it has been taken advantage of by few if any students and may merely represent nothing more than a sympathy in this direction by certain members of the departments of history, government, and English.

GEORGE WASHINGTON UNIVERSITY, Washington, D. C.

Robert W. Bolwell and James H. Coberly (American literature).

A "comprehensive" major program in "American Thought and Civilization" leading to a B. A. and including a special course, a Master of Arts degree in "American Literary and Cultural History," and a doctoral program in certain aspects of American studies.

1936 (undergraduate); 1938 (graduate).

Undergraduate 24; M. A. 3; Ph. D. 2.

ADMINISTRATION: The undergraduate major program at George Washington is administered as a quasi-department with control of curriculum in the hands of a chairman and staff drawn from the field of American literature. The program was formed, however, with the collaboration of the American history staff. Full departmental status is not considered valid or expedient.

UNDERGRADUATE PROGRAM: The field-of-study major in "American Thought and Civilization" requires no specific number of credit hours and no specific program of courses; the major examination replaces all the traditional quantitative and qualitative requirements for a major. However, freshmen and sophomores in the program are expected to take two semesters of American history, two semesters of introductory American literature, and one semester of modern European history. In the junior and senior years the student is strongly urged to take a two-semester course in social history of the United States, and a two-semester course in American literature. A wealth of recommended courses and elective courses in arts, literature, drama, poetry, political geography, economic history, philosophy, government, religion, diplomatic history, journalism, constitutional history, biography, and folk arts is open to the interested candidate, who must guide his studies towards the "comprehensive" examination given in the senior year. The one course required of all upperclass concentrators is a two-semester proseminar to review and coordinate the materials in the major field.

UNDERGRADUATE COURSE: The conference-type proseminar for majors, taken in the senior year, brings together all the materials of all the separate courses. Ralph H. Gabriel's The Course of American Democratic Thought is used as a text, but not in the usual sense of a text, by all students. In addition to Gabriel, Crane Brinton's The Shaping of the Modern Mind, Perry Miller's American Thought: Civil War to World War I, and five Amherst Problems in American Civilization pamphlets are required reading. The organization of the course consists of a "warp" of ten historical periods and a "woof" of ten constant culture features, specifically geography, government, philosophy, literature, arts and crafts, immigration, history, education, religion, and communication of ideas. By shuttling each of the culture features across each of the historical periods something like the "whole cloth" of America emerges. The student must prove that he has mastered the material in a comprehensive examination, requiring two afternoons to complete, at the end of his senior year. The proseminar for majors is not open to other students, but sometimes new graduate students are allowed to audit the course for review and "backgrounding."

GRADUATE PROGRAM: The course of study leading to a Master of Arts degree in "American Literary and Cultural History" (Columbian College) is in general a combination of American literature and American social history with the addition of pertinent materials from the fields of philosophy, education, and art. Students admitted to the program must have completed an undergraduate major in history (with American history as a major part), "American Thought and Civilization," or English literature (with introductory courses in American literature and American history). The professor of American literature acts as adviser to all students taking the program. Collaborating with him are the professor of American history and other faculty colleagues in closely related fields. In addition to language requirements, etc., candidates for the degree are required to take twelve semester hours of seminar study (half in American history and half in American literature), to take twelve semester hours of advanced courses selected and recommended from the fields of American history, literature, philosophy, education, and art, to prepare a thesis in any of the foregoing fields, or in some combination of them, and to pass a Master's examination written in the combined fields of American literature and cultural history. Use is made of existing courses and seminars. Formerly four out of five candidates for the degree in "American Literary and Cultural History" entered with an undergraduate training in literature; in recent years the number of literature majors has declined and the number of those entering from a background of history, journalism, or directly from the government service, has increased. Less than one quarter of those taking the degree go on to the Ph. D. program, most ending their study with the M. A. and going into secondary school teaching or government work.

The Ph. D. is directed by the Graduate Council, quite separate-- except for faculty--from the other divisions of the University. Dr. Robert W. Bolwell of the English department directs doctoral research in "American Literary Nationalism" in succeeding periods. At present this is the only topic of research at the doctoral level. Ph. D. candidates writing dissertations in American literature are required to have a competence in the following fields: (a) American literature, (b) American intellectual and social history, (c) American economic and political history, (d) English literature and social history since the Renaissance, and (e) European intellectual and social history since the Renaissance.

COMMENT: The aim of the undergraduate major at George Washington is "to give the student at the time of his baccalaureate graduation a coordinated knowledge of American culture with its background of intellectual and social tradition, in order that he may meet the activities and interests of modern life with superior understanding and conviction." The program in American studies in existence at the present time in the undergraduate college and in the graduate school is considered successful and is viewed favorably by the faculty. Special aspects of the program at George Washington include the permissive, "comprehensive" major (which in spite of the responsibility it places on the student, reportedly attracts only students of average ability); the interestingly ambitious undergraduate proseminar; and the domination of all aspects of the program by the literary interests (note especially the doctoral program wherein only literary topics may be elected).

GOUCHER COLLEGE, Baltimore, Maryland.

William L. Neumann (history).

An American civilization major program leading to the B. A. degree, and including one course in American civilization.

1951.

10 candidates for B. A.

ADMINISTRATION: The American civilization program at Goucher has quasi-departmental status with control of the program in the hands of an independent chairman aided by a steering committee. Creation of the department was the result of a joint effort by the history department and the administration. Full departmental status is not considered valid or expedient in a small college organized the way Goucher is.

UNDERGRADUATE PROGRAM: The major in American civilization is an interdepartmental major including humanities, social sciences, and history. There are no prerequisites in the freshman and sophomore years for the major, but course work is patterned to the needs and interests of the individual student. In the junior and senior years, however, a minimum of two courses in American history and two in American literature are required. No new courses have been added to traditional departments as a result of the program in American studies, but a special research course has been suggested by some. Number of students in the major, compared with other majors, is about average.

UNDERGRADUATE COURSE: A special integration course is given in the third term of the senior year in preparation for the comprehensive examination. The form and content of the course have not yet been stabilized though the purpose is to give students a new approach to American civilization. No text is used and content is left to the discretion of the instructor.

COMMENT: The American civilization program is offered with the hope that it will assist the student in integrating a broader body of useful materials than does a departmental major, and that it may provide a better and more interesting major for a particular group of students. Faculty attitude towards the major has been mixed. Both program and course in American civilization at Goucher have remained unstabilized and formless; enrollment has fluctuated with personnel changes. Lately, however, a marked increase in enrollment may furnish the needed opportunity for remedying this instability.

GRINNELL COLLEGE, Grinnell, Iowa.

Charles G. Cleaver (English), Chairman of the American Studies Committee.

An American studies program leading to the B. A., including twelve hours in American studies seminars.

1957.

12 majors.

ADMINISTRATION: The Grinnell College program has been established under quasi-departmental administration. A steering committee,
representative of several fields, is responsible for direction; it must
submit major changes to the dean of the college and to the executive
council of the faculty.

UNDERGRADUATE PROGRAM: This is an interdepartmental
major including humanities, social sciences, and history. It requires
a concentration of work in history and literature, as well as distribution
of work across several other fields, which may include art, philosophy,
religion, political science, economics, and sociology. The program
requires 46 to 48 hours in contrast to an average requirement of 30
hours in a traditional discipline. In freshman and sophomore years,
the major student is required to take modern European history, American history, American literature, as well as prerequisites of such
other courses as he chooses from a list of options. In junior and senior years, the major must take three seminars in American studies.

UNDERGRADUATE COURSES: Three seminars must be taken by
majors in the last three of their eight semesters. (The seminars are
also open to other qualified students.) The first seminar, offered in the
spring of 1958, covers the period 1607-1828; the second, 1828-1901;
the third, 1901 to the present. Each seminar is organized around selected critical issues central to its period. For example, the first
seminar will examine ideas and values represented by Jonathan Edwards
as opposed to those represented by Benjamin Franklin; from four to six
such issues, as they involve art, literature, music, politics, economics,
etc., will be studied in each seminar. A different professor (two from
English, one from history) will be in charge of each seminar, but each
plans to make occasional use of other members of the faculty. At the
outset of each semester, students will read certain books in common
(Commager's The American Mind, Riesman's The Lonely Crowd,
Kennan's American Diplomacy, for example) and the instructor will
employ the customary discussion method of teaching. Thereafter, students will present a series of papers, each an interdisciplinary study of
an issue; two students will be assigned to each topic, so that when papers are read in class, the two points of view on the issue will be represented and will catalyze discussion.

COMMENT: The Grinnell program is designed to counteract the
implication of the traditional curriculum to the effect that human be-

havior is departmentalized. It aims to "show the manner in which political, economic, social, philosophical, and imaginative acts are related to one another." Although the program is only in its first year, the responsible committee is encouraged by the fact that its majors are above the institution's average in ability. Faculty reaction is described as mixed, yet there is little hostility, and support of the college's executive council is apparently firm. Professor Cleaver believes that the program would gain in balance through the addition of a course in American music in the music department.

GUSTAVUS ADOLPHUS COLLEGE, St. Peter, Minnesota.

Gerhard Alexis (English).

An American studies program leading to the B. A., including a course in American studies.

1949.

One major.

ADMINISTRATION: The American studies program at Gustavus Adolphus is administered by the department of area studies and directed by a one-man committee, Professor Alexis of the English department. (An interdepartmental steering committee was originally set up, but other members have not continued to take an active part in the program's direction.) English and sociology were active in instituting the program. Although other departments have contributed little to the direction of the program, the attitude of the faculty toward it is felt to be generally favorable. Professor Alexis believes the college is not large enough to justify departmental status for the program.

UNDERGRADUATE PROGRAM: The program is best described as a flexible interdepartmental major that includes humanities, social sciences, history, and natural science, as well, if the student's interest and background so dictate. Like all students at Gustavus, a major is required to take a year of social science as a freshman. Upper division requirements for the major include one semester of American philosophy, two semesters of American literature, and two semesters of American history or history of Western civilization. (The student may include both.) Although a specified grade average is not required for admission to the program, it does attract students of better than average intellectual ability.

The addition of courses in American philosophy and American art to the curricula of traditional departments has been largely a consequence of the program.

UNDERGRADUATE COURSE: A minority of students in the course are majors in the program, so the course is designed as a liberal education offering rather than as a training for majors. Its two semesters are individually organized: the first, according to selected topics arranged chronologically, up to the twentieth century; the second, dealing with contemporary America, according to two broad categories of topics--domestic and external, or international, aspects of the culture. Professor Alexis combines lecture and discussion in his conduct of the course; he uses slides and recordings, and he brings in for guest lectures (one each) members of the music, art, geology, and business administration departments. (The latter is a lawyer and discusses constitutional law.)

The course draws on art, architecture, geology, history, history of science, literature, music, philosophy, religion. Students are required to read approximately fifteen books (many of them in paperback edition) a semester, ranging from Franklin's Autobiography to Burl Ives' Songbook.

COMMENT: The aim of both course and program is to counter the narrowness of specialization. Both course and program attract high-ability students: the course, considerably more of them than the program. Professor Alexis believes that the numbers who elect the course (15 to 25) indicate that the program would have a larger enrollment if its nature were better understood by students at the outset of their college careers.

HARVARD UNIVERSITY, Cambridge, Massachusetts.

Undergraduate Program, Sterling Dow (archeology); Graduate Program, Louis Hartz (history).

Major in "American History and Literature" leading to the A. B. degree. Graduate program in American civilization leading to Ph. D. degree and including a half course.

Undergraduate program, 1906; Graduate program, 1937.

Undergraduate program, 80 (approx.); graduate program, 25 (limited to this number).

ADMINISTRATION: Each of these programs is administered by a chairman and an interdepartmental degree-recommending committee with control of the curriculum but not of budget and staff.

UNDERGRADUATE PROGRAM: This is essentially an honors program in American history and literature, though several other courses in related fields may be counted toward the major. There are no specific course requirements for majors in this area, and there is no American studies course as such. The heart of the program is the tutorial system. Sophomores meet individually once a week. These students agree on a heavy and sustained reading program with their tutors and often prepare short papers based on this reading. Seniors are required to submit an honors essay of about 20,000 words. Though enrollment in this program is obviously limited by the fact that it is virtually an honors program, it still ranks among the second five majors chosen by the students.

UNDERGRADUATE COURSE: Although there is no undergraduate course in American civilization as such, it should be pointed out that the heavy use of the tutorial system amounts to a course in guided study for all undergraduates in the program.

GRADUATE PROGRAM: This is designed to provide an opportunity for a limited number of exceptionally able graduate students to acquire a Ph. D. in American civilization. This graduate program is a highly individualized one with emphasis upon the needs and interests of each student. The essence of this program is essentially an attempt to allow the student to pursue an individual course of research and, in preparation for it, to take such courses as he chooses for their relevance and usefulness for his purposes. Specific requirements state that all candidates must prepare: (1) the field of social and economic history of the United States; (2) at least two of the following fields: literature, political and constitutional thought, religion and theology, or philosophy (all these being American fields); and (3) at least one of the following: the history of science and learning, the fine arts, religion and theology, philosophy, political theory, education, European literature, or other subjects relevant to the student's thesis. The total of the fields must be five, of which one can be "written off" through previous course work or other means. It would be in error to imply from this set of requirements any strict emphasis on course work per se. On the contrary, efforts have reportedly been made to release the student from dependence on the mechanical aspects of graduate study, to encourage him in the pursuit of self-education, and to allow him to build a program suited to his own needs. Although these efforts have admittedly failed in some cases, one sees in them a frank effort to imitate what is considered best in European institutions of higher learning.

There are two basic examinations in the program for the Ph. D. in American civilization at Harvard. The first is a preliminary four-hour written examination, usually taken at the end of the first year, on a single topic, such as literature or social history, in a given period in European history. This examination is designed to insure a proper Western civilization background for the study of American culture. The second examination is a two-hour oral examination on three fields in American studies, in one of which the candidate is examined for one hour. The major American field is usually the counterpart of the field selected for emphasis on the preliminary examination. A fourth American field is written off on the basis of course work.

GRADUATE COURSE: The University does offer a half-course open only to candidates for the Ph. D. degree in American civilization and which is taken by many of these students. The content of this course varies from year to year depending upon the instructor giving the course and the interests of the students taking it. The emphasis in on informality, and the staff consists of members of the governing committee plus a fellow in history.

COMMENT: The undergraduate program is designed to provide a major that will cut across departmental lines, especially in the areas of history and literature. Its emphasis on honors work and the tutorial system insures the high quality of performance. The aims of the graduate program are well expressed in the words of a former chairman, "We believe that the conventional departments can do most of the things that are needed in American scholarship and that our function is simply to take care of those few students who have the ability and the interest to tackle subjects which for one reason or another cannot easily be covered in one of the regular departmental programs." With only one or two exceptions, Harvard Ph. D.'s in American civilization are now engaged in college or university teaching and research principally in the fields of literature and history. Graduates of the program include such well-known scholars as Henry Nash Smith, Daniel Aaron and E. S. Morgan. The program, on both undergraduate and graduate levels, is interesting as a successful example of the type of permissive curriculum often unsuccessful at other institutions. This success is easily traceable to the factors of limited enrollment, insistence on high quality in students admitted, and generous amounts of time given to guidance and supervision of each student's program.

HILLSDALE COLLEGE, Hillsdale, Michigan.

W. H. Roberts (history).

An American civilization program leading to the B. A., including a
course.

1954.

12 candidates for the B. A.

ADMINISTRATION: The program at Hillsdale is part of the history
department, directed by a history professor and a steering committee
consisting of official representatives of other departments (political
science, sociology, humanities). Departmental status for the program
is considered valid.

UNDERGRADUATE PROGRAM: Hillsdale's program can best be
described as an interdepartmental major including humanities, social
sciences, and history. A basic, two-semester course in American civilization, offered in the history department, is required of all freshmen. In the junior-senior years, the major is required to take 12
semester hours in history or political science, 6 in economics or sociology, 6 in philosophy or education, and 6 in the humanities. History
has proved the most popular of the traditional fields of concentration
within the program. Enrollment indicates that the program is among
the second five in frequency of choice as a major, sharing that rank with
economics, English, and psychology. Graduates of the program most
frequently go into teaching and law.

UNDERGRADUATE COURSE: The basic course is required of all
freshmen at Hillsdale and so is aimed at contributing to liberal education of all students rather than to the training of majors. Designed to
provide a new approach to American civilization, it deals with contemporary culture as well as the past and includes materials from art,
architecture, history, literature, music, philosophy, religion, and
history of science and technology. Text and syllabus, as well as selected document materials in the library, are used. The several sections
of the course are taught by two historians, a political scientist, a professor of philosophy, and the dean of men, all of whom combine lecture
and discussion methods, supplemented by visual aids and occasional
lectures by guests.

COMMENT: The program is designed to acquaint students with
the political, social, religious, economic, and cultural ideas and ideals

that have influenced American civilization from its beginning to the present. The attitude of the faculty of Hillsdale is generally favorable to the program, and the attitude of the students toward the program became noticeably more positive when the introductory American civilization course became a requirement for all freshmen. Although the only fixed course requirements (outside the introductory course) are in the humanities, there still seems to exist a marked emphasis on the history-government approach, which may account to some degree for the appeal the program has for pre-legal students.

HOBART AND WILLIAM SMITH COLLEGES, Geneva, New York.

John Lydenberg (English and American studies).

Program leading to the B. A. and including senior seminar for majors.

1955.

12 candidates for the B. A.

ADMINISTRATION: An interdepartmental committee composed of those interested in the American field is responsible for the administration of the American studies offering.

UNDERGRADUATE PROGRAM: The only special requirements of this major include American history, literature, and politics as upper division electives and a senior integrating seminar. General requirements include 36 hours in relevant fields.

UNDERGRADUATE COURSE: The senior seminar mentioned above has recently been offered for the first time; therefore no report can be given on its nature.

COMMENT: Thus far this program has profited from the enthusiastic backing of the English department, but has suffered from a reported indifference on the part of much of the faculty and from the hostility of the history department. One complaint concerning the motivation of American studies majors involves their wish to escape the concentrated work of traditional departments. This does not seem surprising in light of the extremely light major requirements (above) and the absence until recently of any special course at all in the field.

HOLLINS COLLEGE, Hollins College, Virginia.

G. Cary White (sociology), Chairman of the American Society Course.

No degree program in American civilization is offered; however, a special American civilization course is required of all candidates for the A. B. degree.

1951.

ADMINISTRATION: The American society course is offered under the sponsorship of the division of social sciences, and directed by an independent chairman. A steering committee, consisting of representatives of branches of the social sciences, assists the chairman.

UNDERGRADUATE COURSE: Each member of the division of social sciences takes full responsibility for one or several sections into which the course is divided. History, history of science and technology, and religion are the principal disciplines included in the course. The primary emphasis is on the study of institutions such as the family, education, religion, government, economics, etc. Emphasis is also placed upon study of factors in social change and upon class and caste structures of American society. The course commences with a reading assignment in Stuart Chase's The Proper Study of Mankind, and concludes with a consideration of values in American life. Use is made of films and public lectures.

COMMENT: The aims of the course are (1) to help the student at the beginning of her college career to see, as a whole, the society of which she is a part; (2) to develop a positive but intelligently founded appreciation for its fundamental values; and (3) to acquire perspective upon its problems and dilemmas. The course is not a conventional survey of the social sciences. It involves a study of (a) the significant characteristics of our major social institutions; (b) their historical origin and development; (c) their inter-relationships in the total structure of our society; (d) the processes which have brought about significant changes in our social life; (e) the effect upon the individual of caste and class membership and ethnic origin; and (f) the values which underlie our social system. The attitude of the faculty toward the course has been favorable.

KANSAS STATE TEACHERS COLLEGE, Emporia, Kansas.

Claude E. Arnett, Head, Social Science Division.

No degree programs are offered to students at any level; two courses, however, are required in American Civilization of all candidates for the B. A. or the B. S. in education.

1945.

ADMINISTRATION: The American civilization courses are offered under the sponsorship of the social science division. Even though there is no American studies program per se to be administered, the idea of an independent American studies department is considered both valid and expedient, and means have been considered to make the American studies administration more autonomous. In addition to the social science division, members of the history and education staff were influential in initiating the American civilization courses. The teaching load has thus far been carried by faculty trained in history, political science, and sociology.

UNDERGRADUATE COURSES: The first course, offered at the sophomore level, is taught by faculty trained in history and political science, and carries the broad objective of making the student aware of both the native and European backgrounds of American civilization. Brunn and Commager's Europe and America Since 1492 is used as a text, and material from the following fields is included: art, architecture, history, history of science and technology, literature, music, philosophy, religion, sociology, and psychology. The course is divided into about four sections, and the emphasis among these materials varies according to the instructor, each section being taught by only one person. The method is a combination of lecture and discussion based on chronologically arranged topics which follow outlines prepared by the instructor. Course enrollment averages about 200 students.

The second course, offered at the senior level, emphasizes the problem approach to the study of contemporary American society. Barnes and Ruedi, The American Way of Life, is used as a text. Problems are broached through the impetus of student initiative, and the discussion method is heavily relied upon. As in the sophomore course, each section of the course is taught by a single instructor, hence reflects an understandable variety in stress; in the staff for this course, training in sociology predominates, but materials are introduced from the fields of: history, history of science and technology, literature, philosophy, religion, sociology, and psychology. Course enrollment averages 150 students.

COMMENT: Since there is no program as such, the aims of the American studies activities can be accurately expressed as those involved in the two courses: to make the student aware of his native and European background, to introduce him to some of the problems of contemporary America and to suggest some solutions for them -- past and present. Because these courses are so broadly required, it might be fairly stated that these aims are those of the College itself, and furthermore, that the College has reached the conclusion that these aims can best be attained through an American studies-social science emphasis applied to the general education program. The faculty attitude toward these courses ranges from mixed to favorable. Because the courses are required, enrollment figures have no significance nor do student interests, motivations, and quality. The typical graduate is, of course, a teacher. In evaluation, the only negative aspect of these courses might be their stress of the social sciences at the expense of the humanities. Sociology, political science, and psychology receive more attention here than in the typical American civilization course. This lack of balance is to some extent righted by curricular requirements in the humanities division, which include English composition, English literature, and a speech-art-music option; also, American history is required of all prospective elementary school teachers.

MARIETTA COLLEGE, Marietta, Ohio.

Robert L. Jones (history).

One undergraduate course.

1946.

ADMINISTRATION: In so far as there is an American civilization program at all, it is a part of the department of history, under the control of the chairman and staff of that department. The general faculty is indifferent to the program, accepting the opinion of the department of history; that department itself has only qualified admiration for the idea of American civilization, feeling that too great a concentration on American civilization may exclude other important subject matter.

UNDERGRADUATE COURSE: The primary function of this course is to integrate the work in the fields of American history and literature. It is taken by seniors only, and by males two to one. The course consists of selected topics arranged chronologically and is administered by lecture by a single individual and by discussion. The students are expected to do individual research and to produce a term paper. The scope is from colonial times to the present, and texts include Curti's and the Heath Series.

COMMENT: This is simply one course which is employed by a traditional department in order to tie separate offerings together more closely. There is no reason to believe that any expansion toward American studies is intended.

MARY BALDWIN COLLEGE, Staunton, Virginia.

Martha Grafton, Dean of the College.

An American studies major program leading to the B. A. degree.

1950.

1 candidate for the B. A.

ADMINISTRATION: The American studies major at Mary Baldwin is administered separately for each major student by a committee chosen from traditional departments. The departments of history, economics, and sociology were all active in instituting the offering. Separate departmental status for American studies is considered neither valid nor expedient.

UNDERGRADUATE PROGRAM: A student majoring in American studies is required to complete, if possible to schedule, a one-semester course in modern art in the U. S., a two-semester course in principles of economics, a two-semester course in American literature, a two-semester course in U. S. history, a one-semester course in American thought, and a two-semester course in American government. Three additional one-semester courses must be elected from among the following: ornithology, field botany, modern drama, labor problems, British and American poetry, American foreign policy, Southern history, representative Americans, contemporary events, the community, and marriage and the family. No course in foreign civilization is required, and there is no extra-curricular program. The major in American studies must also complete, under the direction of her major committee, a senior thesis or project dealing with some aspect of American civilization. A three-hour written examination covering all aspects of her major field, and a one-hour oral examination emphasizing matters per-taining to her senior project, complete the requirements.

COMMENT: The American Studies program is intended to acquaint the better-than-average student with a comprehensive picture of the traditions, problems, and accomplishments of American civilization. The program is carefully tailored to the needs and interests of the indi-vidual student, and deviation from the program is possible if approved by the student's advisory committee. The required minimum hour load is about equal to comparable major programs in literature or history; nevertheless, since 1953 only one student per year has majored in the program. The unusual choice in supplying an option in the natural sci-ences (ornithology, field botany) should be noted as an unique aspect of this program.

MARY WASHINGTON COLLEGE, Fredericksburg, Virginia.

Robert L. Hilldrup (history).

An American civilization major program, leading to the B. A. degree, and including one course in American civilization.

1950.

No candidates for the B. A.

ADMINISTRATION: The "American Ideals and Institutions" major at Mary Washington has interdepartmental status and is administered independently by a chairman attached to the department of history. The departments of history, literature, art, political science, sociology, and economics were all active in the creation of the program; and they all participate in it. Full departmental status for the program is not con-sidered valid.

UNDERGRADUATE PROGRAM: The interdepartmental major in "American Ideals and Institutions" offers courses in American art, lit-erature, history, government, economics, and sociology. The social sciences form the core of the major, but American contributions to the humanities are not neglected. Prerequisites in the freshman and soph-omore years for a major in the program are courses in American his-tory, American literature, American government, and American art. In the junior and senior years the major must take a two-semester

- 51 -

course in the history of civilization, a two-semester course in the social and intellectual history of the U. S., a two-semester course in diplomatic history of the U. S., a two-semester course in advanced studies in American literature, and eighteen additional semester hours of work elected from courses in the history of the South, constitutional history of the U. S., economic development of the U. S., economic geography of the Americas, principles and problems of sociology, economic principles and problems, state government of Virginia, propaganda and politics, and race relations.

UNDERGRADUATE COURSE: The course in "Social and Intellectual History of the United States," created especially for the program in American studies, is required of all majors either in their junior or senior years. It is conducted by a single individual who may invite other faculty members to lecture. Class discussion is a vital part of the course, and term papers are required, and are presented in class. It should be made clear that, in spite of its title, this course represents more than an ordinary history offering. The staff includes representatives of the departments of art, economics, English, political science as well as history; and a real attempt is made to cover all major phases of American history -- literary and esthetic as well as social and intellectual.

COMMENT: The aim of the "American Ideals and Institutions" program is to give students, especially those going into teaching in the public schools, journalism, social work, or the law, a thorough coverage of all aspects of American culture, including the physical and economic geography of the United States. Faculty attitude toward the program has been favorable. Enrollment, however, has never exceeded three in any one year, partly, perhaps, because it is almost impossible to take the courses required to obtain a major and still work into the program the hours in education, including practice teaching, which the student needs for certification. The course in "Social and Intellectual History of the United States" has attracted more students (eight in 1955-1956) than are majoring in "American Ideals and Institutions," but it has not been popular as an elective.

MIAMI UNIVERSITY, Oxford, Ohio.

William E. Alderman, Dean, College of Arts and Science.

Undergraduate major program.

1948.

No exact figures available; reported as "very few."

ADMINISTRATION: This program is administered by an informal committee made up of the chairmen of interested departments: history, literature, government, geography, and music. It was these same departments which established the program in 1948 and which have run it in very much the same manner ever since. Classed as an interdepartmental major in the humanities, the program is carried out entirely through the auspices of the existing departments. The idea of a more formalized character has seemed either unnecessary or invalid.

UNDERGRADUATE PROGRAM: There is no specifically American civilization course. The program consists of courses from other departments which are combined according to the following credit allotments: 12 hours American literature, 18 hours chosen from history, geography, government, and music. At least one course in each area is required. The major is among the smallest five in the college; there are few major students per year and sometimes none at all.

COMMENT: The small number of interested students in spite of a reportedly favorable attitude towards this program on the part of faculty and administration seems to indicate some lack. Possibly this might consist in the absence of any real identity, either in a special course or in administrative status, for the program, and in its dependence entirely on the good will of the participating departments. Also to be noted is the apparent lack of participation by the social sciences, although this may be at least in part a matter of definition.

MILLS COLLEGE, Oakland, California.

Laurence Sears (American philosophy and political theory), Franklin Walker (American literature).

American studies program leading to B. A. and including two undergraduate courses.

1944.

5 candidates for the B. A.

ADMINISTRATION: Mills College has offered an undergraduate major program in American studies since 1944. With the participation of endowed chair-holders in American history, literature, and philosophy, the program has quasi-departmental status under the direction of its chairman. The number of students taking majors in American civilization is small, although the program is well supported by the College administration, and its chairman indicates his feeling that more formal independent (departmental) status is not necessary or advisable. At present, the College is using funds granted by the Carnegie Corporation to experiment with further integration of traditional disciplines and with additions to the program. One new course has been added (see below -- "Patterns of American Thought"), and plans were announced in 1955 to develop a post-doctoral seminar for college teachers.

UNDERGRADUATE PROGRAM: The program for the A. B. begins with the freshman course described below, "An Introduction to the Study of Man through the Use of American Materials." It then requires courses in American political and social history, literature, political theory, and philosophy. Beyond the minimum in these fields, the student selects additional courses in American history, literature, North American art and music, sociology, government, and economics, the largest number of offerings being in the social sciences. The present availability of funds for experiment and development is encouraging further growth of inter-disciplinary activity.

UNDERGRADUATE COURSES: The freshman course in American civilization, of two semesters' duration, is taught collaboratively by specialists in American history, literature, philosophy, and the arts. It is organized to consider a series of social, intellectual, and moral problems in the light both of historic and of present documents and viewpoints. In the first semester, which raises questions of personal and intellectual values, the approach is primarily through literature and philosophy. The second semester's topics (e.g., "Some Social and Economic Problems in an Industrial Society") deal principally with political and social aspects of citizenship. Readings of primary and secondary documents are required, from novels to Congressional reports. No single text or anthology is used throughout, but students purchase some of the materials and use the library for the remainder. A new course, "Patterns of American Thought," given to seniors, is similarly organized and taught.

COMMENT: The whole program, according to a Bulletin of the College, "aims to strengthen the student's love for America and make concrete her concepts of the American values which are so important to the world today. We believe that the best Americans are those who know their country and its ideals most intimately." The College also observes that it sees American culture in an organic relationship to the whole of Western civilization, rather than as an exclusive or provincial phenomenon.

It is to be observed that the College considers its American studies offerings to be a significant part of its educational program. Its endowed chairs, the embodiment of an essential part of the program in its required A. B. curriculum for all students, and the inclusion of work in at least three principal fields of American studies for the major -- these indicate the measure of the College's interest in the program. The awareness of a past limitation in studies of the non-literary arts is suggested by the recent addition of a leading music and art scholar as a regular participant in the program. Furthermore, the proposal to conduct post-doctoral courses for members of the faculty in order to train them in disciplines not included in their own backgrounds (a proposal made in connection with the Carnegie grant) represents an unusual devotion to the interdisciplinary idea.

MONMOUTH COLLEGE: Monmouth, Illinois.

F. G. Davenport (history).

No degree program offered, but two courses in the field.

1947 (Course I). Course II added in 1953.

ADMINISTRATION: The American culture course is offered within the history department and is directed by the head of the department. The seminar in American civilization is offered within the history, English, and sociology departments. The head of the history department is the permanent chairman, but the direction of the offerings is determined by the three heads of departments concerned.

UNDERGRADUATE COURSES: "History of American Culture" is a three hour lecture course built around the central concept of the "American democratic impulse." The subject material of the course goes beyond the traditional area of history, including art, architecture, history of science, literature, music, philosophy, and religion. No text is used, and lectures are supplemented by readings, slides, etc.

"Seminar in American Civilization" is restricted to three honor students from each of the three participating disciplines and is offered each year. The seminar is an interdepartmental venture taught by representatives of the three departments. The students may take this seminar for credit in any one of the three departments, by properly emphasizing material from it. Each year the seminar centers around a different theme and individual research papers. No textbook is used.

COMMENT: The aims of the courses are listed as follows: (1) to acquaint the student with the historical developments of the culture of which he is an integral part, (2) to stimulate wide-reading on the multiple phases of our social and cultural history, (3) to aid in the integration of the student's educational experiences in the liberal arts. The courses, as presently structured, have attracted mainly above-average students. They are successful, and due to this the interdepartmental seminar idea has expanded to include other combinations of departments such as a course in Mediterranean culture conducted on a modified seminar plan by the departments of art and foreign languages. The history department has also added an independent study course in American biography which can be taken for either history or English credit.

MOUNT HOLYOKE COLLEGE, South Hadley, Massachusetts.

Mary S. Benson, Chairman for the Major.

Major in American studies leading to an A. B. degree; and a certificate program, including graduate courses, for foreign students.

1942.

24 majors in American studies.

ADMINISTRATION: This program is in charge of a chairman of the major who is assisted by an advising committee representing traditional departments. The make-up of this advising committee varies with the particular program of the individual major student.

UNDERGRADUATE PROGRAM: The major consists of an interdepartmental program of courses in history, literature, art, philosophy, religion, political science, economics, sociology and geography. In addition to a full year survey course in American history, students majoring in American studies are expected to take a full year course in American literature and two advanced seminar courses in American history. They are also required to take work in at least one other related field. The major ranks about sixth or so among the fields chosen at Mount Holyoke. It does not include any special course or courses in American studies.

GRADUATE PROGRAM: Theoretically, Mt. Holyoke offers the M. A. degree in American culture under a program tailored to suit the needs of the individual student and directed by staff from the English and history departments. Practically, however, since no one has taken advantage of this program within recent memory, it is not considered an active portion of the curriculum. The explanation for this lack of interest rests with the attachment of graduate students, via assistant-ships, to the various established departments. Since the American culture program has no departmental status, it has not been able to appoint assistants and has thereby failed to attract graduate interest.

A "Certificate in American Studies" is awarded annually to about three-to-five foreign students who pursue a program made up of both graduate and undergraduate courses amounting to 18 hours credit in courses pertaining primarily to the U. S. These students may not be registered for the B. A. or M. A. and their program is administered by the Foreign Student Adviser.

COMMENT: This program is designed to help the student gain a better understanding of this country and the world of which this country is a part. It is believed that these aims can best be realized by combining work in several departments. Indeed, the college offers a wide variety of courses in many departments that have relevance to America and that may be included in the major. There is, however, no formal attempt to integrate these materials, at least in the form of a special American studies course.

NEW YORK UNIVERSITY, New York, New York.

Henry B. Parks, Director, and Oscar Cargill, Secretary, American civilization program.

Programs of study leading to the B. A., M. A., and Ph. D. and including a special course and program at the M. A. level.

1944 (graduate); 1945 (undergraduate).

Candidates for the B. A.: 5; for the M. A.: 30; for the Ph. D.: 20.

ADMINISTRATION: Since the American civilization activities at all levels rely on the offerings and requirements of existing departments, curricular and course problems are minor. An independent director, assisted by another faculty member who acts in his absence, administers the program.

UNDERGRADUATE PROGRAM: The student earns a B. A. in American civilization by completing a double major in any two departments within the humanities and social sciences where courses in the American field are offered. This major requires more course work than other undergraduate programs, even though the student is excused from the requirement of a minor. Departments that have proven popular within this major are, in the order of their popularity: English, history, economics, sociology, and government. An undergraduate American civilization course was attempted, but was subsequently dropped due to small enrollment.

GRADUATE PROGRAM: The M. A. is achieved by majoring in a traditional field, usually literature or history, and minoring in selected American courses distributed among various other fields. In addition, a special combination journalism-American civilization M. A. program accounts for about half the enrollment at this level and stresses cultural aspects of journalism for the person who plans a professional career in this field.

Requirements for the Ph. D. begin with a comprehensive written examination in history, after which the candidate may present for his oral examination a double emphasis in any two pertinent departments. Several combinations have been attempted, but the most popular have been literature and history, followed by sociology. Most graduate students in American civilization have undergraduate training in literature (45%), history (30%) or the social sciences and fine arts; often their graduate program involves a change of departmental allegiance, and those who go on to teach do so almost equally in the fields of literature, history, and sociology.

GRADUATE COURSE: A general course is required of first year students in American civilization, covering the main factors in the development of American civilization, with emphasis on the inter-relations of different fields. The course is divided into topics arranged chronologically and is lectured by a single professor. The aim is to provide a general framework for the more detailed work of traditional departmental courses. Course is normally open only to majors in American civilization.

COMMENT: Spokesmen for the program admit that the undergraduate major has been ineffectual, presumably due to the heavy course load and the strong departmental loyalties of the students. The graduate program, after attracting but few students at first, rose markedly after World War II to a peak of some 80 students in 1950, since which time it has declined somewhat and for no apparent reason. Those in charge report some dissatisfaction with dissertation topics (in that many of them might well have occurred under traditional departmental sponsorship); they report no difficulties in placing American civilization degree-holders although they feel that this particular degree has been neither help nor hindrance. Quite noticeable is the strong feeling on behalf of the broad background represented by the civilization approach to study as opposed to a more narrow professional training. The doctoral program, for example, originally required four fields of the student, and the reduction to two fields has not been universally regarded as an improvement.

NORTHERN STATE TEACHERS COLLEGE, Aberdeen, South Dakota.

Sinnia Billups (English).

A single course in American culture.

1947.

ADMINISTRATION: The course in American culture is offered by the English department where it is the responsibility of a single professor, Dr. Billups.

UNDERGRADUATE COURSE: This one-term course is based on lectures and directed discussion by Dr. Billups and requires of its students a term paper encompassing both literature and some other field of study -- art, architecture, music, philosophy, or some other field depending on the student's interest. McDowell's America in Literature is used as a text.

COMMENT: As distinct from the traditional offerings in American literature within the department, this course has for its purpose the suggestion of a broader outlook on the culture of the society which produced the literature. It has proved a popular elective among students of above average ability and has consistently been enrolled up to what is considered the practical limits for the size of such a course (nineteen are enrolled as of 1957).

OHIO WESLYAN UNIVERSITY, Delaware, Ohio.*

B. T. Spencer, Chairman, Department of English.

An undergraduate major leading to the B. A. in American studies; one special undergraduate course.

1947.

2 majors.

ADMINISTRATION: Founded through the efforts of members of the history, English, and philosophy departments, the program is administered by an independent chairman who also serves as adviser to all majors. The special course is offered by a member of the English department and considered, administratively, as a part of the regular offerings of this department. Interdepartmental in nature, the program has been well received by the faculty although there have never been more than one or two majors in a single class. An independent American studies department is held to be valid and expedient only at larger institutions.

UNDERGRADUATE PROGRAM: Described as an interdepartmental major in the humanities, social sciences, and history, the program requires each student to concentrate in one traditional field as well as to include work in art, history, literature, philosophy, sociology, political science, and geography. During the first two years, the student is specifically required to take one-semester courses in economics, American literature, and American government. Upper division course requirements include: 4 semesters of American history; 2 semesters of American literature; and one semester each of American art, philosophy, geography and sociology.

UNDERGRADUATE COURSE: A sophomore-level course, "Studies in American Civilization," has been added to the English department offerings as a result of the program but has not been made a requirement for the major. Each year this course, operated by a single instructor trained in literature, takes up a special topic or theme (such as the frontier, views of foreign travelers, transcendentalism) which is treated by a combination of the cultural and humanistic approaches. The course has proved popular, attracting from 15-20 students annually.

COMMENT: The program at Ohio Weslyan has taken on a double character: partly vocational in that it is recommended particularly for students preparing for foreign service, and partly non-vocational in that it has attracted students with above average abilities who seek a broad, liberal education with an interdepartmental slant. Except for the special course which appears, un-typically, at the sophomore level, the major student is afforded no opportunity to synthesize the multi-departmental offerings which make up his well balanced curriculum.

PARK COLLEGE, Parkville, Missouri.

Jerzy Hauptmann, Director, American Studies Program.

An American studies program leading to the B. A. and including two inter-disciplinary courses in the field.

1953.

5 undergraduate majors.

ADMINISTRATION: The American studies program at Park has an interdivisional character. Its faculty is made up of nine representatives from different teaching fields: art, economics, history, literature, music, philosophy, political science, religion and sociology, and one additional representative from the humanities program. This faculty of ten decides the matters of budget, administration, and curriculum subject to the approval of the proper college authorities. A Director of the program is appointed by the President of the College. No thought has been given to the establishment of a separate American studies department.

UNDERGRADUATE PROGRAM: Requirements for the B. A. in American studies include 2 semesters of American government, 2 semesters of American history, 2 semesters of American literature, 1 semester of American communities (a sociology course), 1 semester of American philosophy, and 2 additional courses from the American studies field to be approved in each case by the American studies faculty. In addition to these courses, the major selects a field of concentration in one of 7 departments (not including at present art and music), where he takes 18 hours of selected courses. The two American studies courses mentioned below are a part of the requirements for graduation. In addition to that a senior thesis is required. At the end of the senior year the student takes a Graduate Record Examination in his field of concentration, and written comprehensive examinations in American studies and in his field of concentration. For the oral comprehensive examination an outside examiner is invited, who becomes a member of the oral examination board, and also delivers the annual college-wide American studies lecture.

UNDERGRADUATE COURSES: (1) During the second semester of the junior year each major takes a course entitled "Readings in American Studies." The first part of the course is based on a joint consideration of the nature of American studies and of the American character. Tape recordings of faculty panels provide the basic method for preparing students for a discussion session. After this part of the course students select special areas for concentrated reading under supervision of members of the American studies faculty and report on their readings to the group. (2) During the senior year an "American Studies Seminar" is offered under the direction of one of the faculty members, with participation of the whole American studies faculty. No textbook is used. The great books approach is utilized, integrated with group discussions on major American studies issues.

COMMENT: Since the program requires a high grade point average, the number of students enrolled is limited, but it is a group interested in intellectual pursuits. The aim is to maintain a program for especially gifted students. The basic shortcoming at the present time is lack of closer integration of art and music into the program. Courses in these disciplines can be taken in fulfillment of the requirement of 6 optional hours, but there exist no courses in these fields specifically geared for the American studies major.

PRINCETON UNIVERSITY, Princeton, New Jersey.

James Ward Smith, (philosophy), Chairman of the Special Program in American Civilization.

Program supplements undergraduate departmental work; the Program offers two courses of its own, a sophomore course and a senior conference.

1942.

99 candidates for the "certificate" in American civilization.

ADMINISTRATION: The "Special Program in American Civilization" at Princeton is administered by a faculty committee composed of representatives from eight participating departments (art, economics and sociology, English, history, philosophy, politics, psychology, and religion) and presided over by a chairman appointed by the President. The program has control of its own course offerings but it has no budget (except an office budget and a publication budget) and makes no appointments to the faculty. Departmental status is considered both invalid and inexpedient; the program originated by the initiative of the faculty and cooperation and support by the participating departments has been excellent. Teaching in the program has been widely distributed among the participating departments.

UNDERGRADUATE PROGRAM: To be eligible for admission to the program, a student must have satisfactorily completed the established requirements for admission to one of the cooperating departments. In the program the student will meet the following requirements: (1) he will take, normally in his sophomore year, "Individualism in American Life"; (2) he will complete the normal departmental program of one of the cooperating departments with such measure of special emphasis on American aspects as the regulations of the department may permit; (3) by the end of the senior year, he will complete at least four one-term courses in the American field, only one of which may be within his department; (4) in his senior year, he will participate in a conference, to be conducted under the direction of the committee, the primary purpose of which will be an integration of his study of American civilization. A student who has met the requirements of the program and who has maintained a suitable average receives upon graduation, in addition to his diploma, a certificate signed by the President of the University testifying to his proficiency in the study of American civilization.

UNDERGRADUATE COURSES: "Individualism in American Life," is a course at the sophomore level, normally required of students in the program and open to others in the college as an elective, which attempts to show how American civilization may profitably be considered as a field of study by exploring a single theme through various modes of expression. The course is lectured by a member of the department of English who was trained in American civilization, assisted in preceptorial meetings by members of the departments of history and sociology. This is a new course, first offered in 1955, and enrollment stands presently at about fifty with no sign that it has proved popular as an elective.

The "Senior Conference," is a course conducted in seminar fashion on some aspect of American civilization and runs through two terms of the senior year. Topics under discussion vary from year to year, although a topic may be offered more than once. The staff of the conference is selected according to the topic. (For examples of topics, see publications, below.) The conference is divided into seminar groups of about eight students each; the students are provided with reading assignments to acquaint them with the general nature of the topic and are then asked to write papers on special aspects of the topic on the basis of bibliographies prepared by the staff. Recognized specialists are invited to address the students in the conference throughout the year.

COMMENT: The Princeton program has from the first been designed to supplement not to supplant the traditional departmental frame of education. It simply induces the student to look at his educational experience from a different perspective than that of his specialty.

Two prizes are offered by the Program: The David F. Bowers Prize, of fifty dollars, is awarded to the student in the American civilization program who does the best work in the annual conference of the program. The Grace May Tilton Prize in Fine Arts, which consists of a certificate and at least one hundred dollars, is awarded for an outstanding thesis by a senior in any of the eight departments collaborating in the program. The thesis must deal wholly or in a major part with some aspect of the fine arts or crafts, past or present, within the territory now embraced by the United States, or elsewhere in the Americas.

The chief glory of the program at Princeton has been the collaborative volumes which have come out of the various senior conferences: David F. Bowers, ed., Foreign Influences in American Life (Princeton, 1944); Stow Persons, ed., Evolutionary Thought in America (Yale, 1950); Donald Egbert and Stow Persons, eds., Socialism and American Life, 2 vols. (Princeton, 1952). A volume is presently envisaged on Religion in American Life under the general editorship of James Ward Smith.

Each year, under a benefaction from a graduate of the program, a symposium, open to the Princeton community, is offered on some topic of current interest in American life. In recent years symposia have been offered on "The Image of America Abroad, " "Anti-Intellectualism in America." These symposia consist of public lectures by invited speakers followed by an evening session open only to students in the program.

Although those who teach in the program feel that it requires more of the student than does a simple departmental major, the students in the program are not above average for Princeton. Students come mainly from English and history with a broad scattering after that; most graduates of the program go into business, law, and graduate work in traditional departments. Princeton has many "straddle" programs and thus was receptive to one in the American field; participation by a faculty member does not seem to help or to hurt his position within his department, largely because the teaching in the program has been widely shared. The program seems to have been both a teaching and a scholarly success at Princeton.

QUEENS COLLEGE OF THE CITY OF NEW YORK, Flushing, N. Y.

Courtney R. Hall (history).

An area program built around existing courses in various departments;
  no courses at present in American civilization; no degree in the
  field as such.

c. 1945.

About six majors in "American Area."

    ADMINISTRATION: An administrative committee of four, ap-
pointed by the President, serves to advise students interested in the
area of American studies: two members are representative of the
Social Science Division, two of the Division of Language, Literature and
the Arts.

    UNDERGRADUATE PROGRAM: There are no special courses in
American civilization. The program at Queens consists of an interdivisional major which spreads across the humanities, social sciences,
and history. A concentration examination is required of majors in
senior year.

    UNDERGRADUATE COURSE: An interdivisional seminar, pri-
marily for majors in the "American Area," is being organized. It will
probably be approved and will then be offered during 1958.

    COMMENT: The purpose of allowing students to select courses
from various departments is to offer the student a cross-section of
fields along American lines without too great specialization. The program is almost entirely permissive; since it is not a program leading
to a degree, this lack is perhaps not so vital as it might be. Nevertheless, the student must depend, it would seem, either on the traditional
department of his choice or on his own initiative to provide him with
whatever integration and cohesion he is to achieve within the field of
American studies.

REED COLLEGE, Portland, Oregon.

Warren I. Susman (history and humanities).

Course in contemporary American civilization.

1955.

ADMINISTRATION: The course in American civilization is offered in the history department, but it is also listed and recommended by the literature-fine arts division.

UNDERGRADUATE COURSE: The course investigates the role, status, and development of the intellectual in American life since 1870. It thus accomplishes a survey of major figures and intellectual movements, in the context of social change. It is taught by a single instructor who meets the class four times a week. The principal mode of instruction is discussion, which, on occasions, is led by the students. Assigned readings involve complete works of leading intellectuals, novels, poetry, criticism, and interpretative studies of American culture and thought. These materials are used to deal with selected problems relevant to the main theme of the course, and are the basis of discussion and student papers.

COMMENT: The course seeks to awaken interest in American culture; to indicate its importance and vitality; and to indicate interrelationships of cultural phenomena. In terms of enrollment and the favorable faculty response, the course is evidently successful. The theme of the course provides a firm basis for integrative study of a variety of cultural materials. At a college noted for the high level of scholarship expected of the students, the course stands out as a challenging and effective example of the thematic approach to American studies.

ROCKFORD COLLEGE AND ROCKFORD MEN'S COLLEGE, Rockford, Illinois.

Mildred F. Berry (American literature), Director of American Studies.

American studies major leading to B. A. and including one special course.

1945.

One major.

ADMINISTRATION: An interdivisional program, American studies at Rockford operates under an independent director without the aid of a steering committee but with the cooperation of the departments of art, economics, philosophy, political science, and sociology. Primary responsibility, however, is carried by the literature and history departments. Faculty attitude toward the program is reported as favorable; no dissatisfaction is noted with the present administrative status.

UNDERGRADUATE PROGRAM: Breadth of curriculum is assured by requiring students to complete a concentration of at least nine hours in three of the following fields: art; philosophy and religion; economics; education and psychology; literature; history; and political science. The only fixed requirements, however, are the basic courses in American literature, history, and government; comparative literature; and European history.

UNDERGRADUATE COURSE: The desired synthesis is provided through a senior seminar, required of all American studies majors, titled "Great Issues in American Life." Based on the culture concept, this course centers on various materials depending on which of the six sections the student enters. Departments represented in the teaching of this course include history, literature, sociology, political science, art and philosophy. This course has proved quite popular as an elective outside the major.

COMMENT: The program is aimed at permitting "a broader approach and a greater opportunity for synthesis of knowledge of American life than is possible in a departmental or divisional major." Carrying with it a special required grade average and a heavier-than-normal course load, the program has attracted only better than average students, and not many of these. Major students tend to emphasize literary and historical aspects of the civilization. Having already produced its own special course, the program is now calling for music and poetry courses directed toward the American scene. A noteworthy feature of the program is a lecture series which has run under the general heading of "Our American Heritage" and which has included such speakers as Merle Curti, Henry S. Commager, and John W. Nason.

ROOSEVELT UNIVERSITY, Chicago, Illinois.*

Kendall B. Taft, Chairman, Department of English.

An undergraduate program leading to the B. A. and including one course in American civilization.

1945.

No data on enrollment.

ADMINISTRATION: The program operates as a quasi-department with an independent chairman. The departments of economics, English, history, philosophy, political science, and sociology participate. Favored with a positive faculty reaction, the program does not look toward a more formalized status.

UNDERGRADUATE PROGRAM: Special requirements for the B. A. in "American Culture" include: 4 semesters of American history, 2 semesters of American literature, 2 semesters of political science, and one semester each of philosophy, economics, sociology, and "The American Heritage." Concentration within one traditional field (usually history or literature) is also required. Finally, the major student must either pass a comprehensive examination in the field of American culture or submit a satisfactory piece of research to an interdepartmental committee or to the staff of a research course in one of the cooperating departments. In spite of these special requirements, students attracted to this major have reflected the institutional average in intelligence. Upon graduation, they have entered such fields as library work, the ministry, teaching, and business.

UNDERGRADUATE COURSE: Required of all major students, but open as a general elective as well, "The American Heritage" is described as "An introductory course dealing with the main currents of American thought and culture. In surveying the most significant aspects of the American heritage, numerous forces, movements, and institutions are discussed, among them: geographic backgrounds, the debt to Europe, Puritanism, religious liberalism, the Revolution, democracy, literary tastes, education, industrialism, social experiments and reform movements, the fine arts, humor and folklore, the Civil War, urbanism, science, imperialism, and internationalism."

COMMENT: The American culture major is offered with the hope that the student will become aware of general trends in American history and culture and will achieve a unified understanding of the American past and present. The program profits from the existence of the comprehensive introductory course, interdisciplinary in nature, described above. The senior requirement of examination or research serves an equivalent role to the more usual senior seminar. Since the establishment of the major, cooperating departments have considerably altered their course offerings so as to adjust to this new program; courses in American art and architecture, however, are still to be introduced.

ROSARY COLLEGE, River Forest, Illinois. *

Sister M. Constanza, Chairman of American Studies.

Major program leading to the B. A.

1944.

4 undergraduate majors.

ADMINISTRATION: Administered by an independent chairman, this program has quasi-departmental status. It was originated through the efforts of the English department; independent departmental status is considered valid but not expedient. A divisional committee assists the chairman.

UNDERGRADUATE PROGRAM: To cite the College Bulletin, "This major is designed for students desiring a survey of the life, the culture, and the traditions of the people of the Western Hemisphere; for teachers of American History, American Literature, and Economics." Specific courses are required in Western civilization, American history, American literature, and the history of art. In addition, the major student must complete at least 46 semester hours in the American area and must submit a senior essay "which will integrate studies made in the various departments... and which will present one phase or one period of American backgrounds and culture." No special course in American civilization is offered.

COMMENT: Although a fairly broad range of elective courses is offered the major student, it is felt that additional courses in American government, music, and art would be of substantial aid to the program. At present, students tend to concentrate in sociology and to enter, upon graduation, the field of elementary teaching.

RUTGERS UNIVERSITY, New Brunswick, New Jersey.

Walter Bezanson, Chairman, Committee on American Civilization.

Undergraduate program leading to a B. A. degree; three courses in
American civilization.

1947.

About 30 majors.

ADMINISTRATION: American civilization at Rutgers has a quasi-
departmental status; it is directed by a steering committee of departmental representatives under the chairmanship of a faculty member who
holds his appointment in American Civilization. In addition to the chairman there is one other faculty appointment in American civilization.

UNDERGRADUATE PROGRAM: In addition to the basic college
requirements in general education, a student to enter the program must
have taken two semesters in "The Development of Western Civilization,"
two semesters in a "Survey of English Literature," and two semesters
in American history. Once in the program a major must take three one-
semester courses in American civilization, four semesters in American
literature, two semesters in advanced courses in American history,
and two semesters of philosophy. The program is presently designed
somewhat as a double major in American history and literature with an
increasing attention toward the behavioral sciences.

UNDERGRADUATE COURSES: "American Civilization 201-202"
is a sophomore course, open to non-majors as an elective, with a socio-
historical point of view; the emphasis of the course is on the concept of
culture and the organization is topical not chronological. Annual enrollment averages fifty to sixty students. "American Civilization 301-302"
is a half-time course, open only to juniors who are majors in American
civilization, organized on a semi-tutorial or preceptorial basis around
individual projects in the source materials. "American Civilization
401-402," open only to seniors who are majors in the program, is run
as a seminar to provide a comprehensive examination of special problems or periods in American civilization (for example, Puritanism, the
Enlightenment, Romantic Democracy, and the impact of European
thinkers).

As now organized, although it must be stressed that all three
courses are newly conceived and are still in the process of change, an
undergraduate major has a course in American civilization at the center
of his program of study during each of the final three years while at
the same time he is doing work in the basic disciplines.

COMMENT: The program at Rutgers shares the aims of a liberal education with the traditional departments in a university and hopes also to give its students a comprehensive knowledge of their own culture and to present a counter force against specialization among both students and faculty. Although it is felt that there might be tactical advantages to a separate organization, the program has been kept interdepartmental in the steady belief that interdepartmentalism is the very essence of area study. Nearly one-third of the graduates of the program go on to graduate school, a percentage that argues for the intellectual success of the undergraduate program. The program at Rutgers has succeeded, it is reported, only with determined and consistent promotion efforts, reaching into the high school level, in order to combat an observed tendency of students to seek vocational training or study in areas already familiar to them. Promotional activities have included film series, as well as an informal student club. Interestingly, it was found that curricular objectives could be more popularly met by requiring a wider latitude of elective courses, a policy which has resulted in students taking more willingly courses which had formerly been required.

ST. MARY'S UNIVERSITY, San Antonio, Texas.

Kenneth J. Carey, Director of American Studies.

Undergraduate major leading to the A. B. degree.

1952.

14 candidates for A. B.

ADMINISTRATION: The American studies program is offered under the auspices of the history, economics, and government departments. The program has been favorably accepted by the faculty; its offerings consist solely of traditional courses in the regular disciplines and these are weighted in the direction of economics and government.

UNDERGRADUATE PROGRAM: The prerequisites for the undergraduate major consist of two semesters each in economics, government, and philosophy, and one course in history and sociology. Two semesters of a foreign language must also be completed by the end of the sophomore year. The courses required of all students as part of their major include two semesters of philosophy and ten semesters in economics and government (six in one discipline and four in the other).

Two additional semesters of a foreign language are also required. There is no special course available for an American studies major.

COMMENT: The American studies program at St. Mary's University is limited to a series of courses offered by the regularly established departments. It has developed in relation to the International Relations Institute and emphasizes especially the influence of foreign civilizations upon American society. Although the economics-political science stress is evident throughout this major, its curriculum also includes requirements in philosophy and foreign language beyond the University minimum. Students in the program are mainly interested in foreign service careers or in teaching. There appears to be some sentiment for a separate department, although no action is apparent at this time.

SAN FRANCISCO STATE COLLEGE, San Francisco, California.

Elias T. Arnesen, Chairman, Humanities Division; James H. Stone, Adviser, American studies major in Humanities.

An American studies major in Humanities; inter-disciplinary courses in American civilization.

1957. Earliest interdisciplinary course, 1943.

No enrollment data as yet.

ADMINISTRATION: The American studies program in the humanities division is under the general direction of the division chairman and the immediate administration of the coordinator of "General Humanities," a quasi-departmental unit of the division which handles its inter-disciplinary courses and programs. All who participate in the American studies program also teach in special fields embraced by the division--literature, philosophy, and foreign languages. On a part-time basis, some instructors are drawn from other divisions of the College, namely creative arts, language arts, and social science. The professional advancement of the humanities division faculty occurs in conjunction both with their special and with their interdisciplinary activities. Although the program requires some work outside the humanities division, the college has authorized the division to offer an inter-department mental A. B. major. At present, therefore, an inter-divisional administration is not thought necessary, and the non-departmental character of the humanities division itself permits inter-disciplinary activities to proceed with a minimum of special administrative apparatus.

UNDERGRADUATE PROGRAM: The program in American studies is one of two patterns leading to the A. B. in General Humanities. It presupposes that the student has completed two general education courses in humanities, one of which deals with American materials; normally, also the student will have taken required general education work in American history and government before starting the major. The program requires two lower division courses in English literature (one a study of forms, the other a survey of the later period of English literary history). Upper division courses are required in "Western Civilization," (intensive selected readings), American literature, art, and thought. Alternative courses are offered to fulfill some of the requirements. The remainder of the 36-unit major is on an elective basis. Certain courses are inter-disciplinary in organization and content among those which are required as well as among the elective offerings (see below). Depending on his use of electives, the student's program will be approximately balanced among history, literature, art, and thought, with a slight concentration in history or literature.

UNDERGRADUATE COURSES: Three types of inter-disciplinary courses in American studies are offered by the College. The first is a lower division course which is required of all students except those who transfer to the College after the freshman year. The course is the second part of a general education humanities sequence entitled "A Study of Values." After encountering literary, philosophic, religious, and artistic works of the ancient world in the first course of the humanities sequence, the student continues his study of values by an intensive examination of three fundamental expressions of American insight and tradition: The Federalist, Horatio Greenough's essays, now published as Form and Function, and Mark Twain's Huckleberry Finn. Other materials may be added at the option of the instructor.

The second type of American studies course is represented by the upper division offering entitled "The American Scene." This course presents a chronological survey of principal tendencies in American literature, thought, and art, seen in the historical context. Textual materials are reserved in the library; slides and recordings are employed to deal with painting, architecture, and music. Other American studies courses of this type are "The Latin-American Scene," and "The California Scene." A principal instructional feature of these courses is the collaboration of three instructors, all participating in the class meetings but one being principally responsible for the work of a given class session.

The third type is more selective and more compactly organized than the second type, so far as subject matter is concerned. One such course, "The American Mind," deals with American philosophic, religious, and social thought. An anthology is used; supplementary reading and reports are required. Unlike the second type of course described above, this course is taught by a single instructor. A new course of this kind was offered in 1957, entitled "Styles of Cultural Expression in America." It deals with the arts and with the principles of expression which have prevailed in notable periods of American life.

The faculty who participate in all three types of course includes individuals whose training and teaching experience has been in literature (with or without concentration in American literature), history, philosophy, or American studies. Many of them are also connected with other (non-American) inter-disciplinary courses, as well as with work in the traditional specialties.

COMMENT: The American studies program aims to reveal patterns of relationship in the social, intellectual, and aesthetic experience of the American people, and the several inter-disciplinary courses seek goals within this context. According to the official description of the program, "Courses in the history of Western civilization and English literature provide a background to, and preclude too provincial an approach to, American culture. Blocks of work in major fields develop a substantial understanding of the content of American experience. Inter-disciplinary courses examine the relationships among parts of American culture and provide a comprehensive view of its whole significance." The program appears to be an outgrowth, in part, of antecedent inter-disciplinary courses; in part, of the interest of individuals trained in American literature and American studies; and, in part, of the presence of faculty trained in traditional fields but possessing broad interests. The program is too new to have indicated its prospects for success at the College; but it does represent, even now, the most highly elaborated series of inter-disciplinary courses on American subjects at any institution of higher learning in the United States.

SARAH LAWRENCE COLLEGE, Bronxville, New York.

Esther Raushenbush, Dean of the College.

Three special series of undergraduate courses. See also below under
    undergraduate and graduate programs.

1928 (undergraduate); 1949 (graduate).

No enrollment data submitted.

ADMINISTRATION: The faculty of the college has control of the curriculum and shares in the determination of the budget and of appointments. The sequence of courses entitled "Studies in American Civilization" comes under the jurisdiction of the division of the social sciences.

UNDERGRADUATE PROGRAM: It would be overstating the case to say that Sarah Lawrence offers a "program" or grants degrees in American civilization. There is, however, the possibility of students working in this area under special advisement. In such cases, students are directed principally towards work in history and the social sciences; literature; and the fine arts.

UNDERGRADUATE COURSES: Nine quarter-long courses, each covering one broad topic in the history of American civilization, have been developed and arranged into three distinct sequences. The student is obliged to follow one sequence throughout a year's work, and will, in the course of the year, study under three different professors representing the areas of history, literature, and political science. These sequences have carried the following titles: (1) "The Conservative Tradition," "The Genteel Tradition," and "Veblen's America"; (2) "Realism at the Turn of the Century," "The Labor Movement," and "Social Darwinism"; (3) "Public Opinion," "Political Parties," and "Writers in Crisis." Designed to offer insight into the essential development of America, the courses are built around intensive reading and discussion of the work of a few key authors. They are offered at the junior-senior level.
More recently, other titles have been added or substituted in these sequences (such as: "The World of Henry Adams," "Interpreters of America," "Resources, Technology and Planning," and "America between Two Wars"), and faculty participation in these series has been broadened to include representatives of such fields as economics, the arts, and psychology.

GRADUATE PROGRAM: First year graduate work is offered at Sarah Lawrence; and, although there is no fixed program in American civilization, a student may choose to concentrate work in this area under special advisement.

COMMENT: The above report is based on what must be called incomplete correspondence with this institution. Although the information reported is believed accurate, it is not sufficiently complete to allow for generalizations.

SKIDMORE COLLEGE, Saratoga Springs, New York.

Grace A. Cockroft (history), Chairman of American Studies; John K. Reeves (English).

Major program leading to the B. A. and including a special senior seminar.

1956.

3 candidates for the B. A.

ADMINISTRATION: American studies is a quasi-department made up of nine representatives of the participating departments of history, English, economics, sociology, government, and art. All of these representatives teach in their respective traditional departments and devote varying portions of their time to the American studies major program.

UNDERGRADUATE PROGRAM: The undergraduate who chooses an American Studies major must satisfy requirements totalling 33 credits in various traditional fields by taking introductory courses designated as "American Core Courses"; she must also take 12 credits in European background courses; she must take advanced-level courses totalling 18 credits in the American and related fields. Finally, she must take the senior seminar in American studies and pass a general examination on the major field. The "core" courses are, in general, introductory courses in such fields as American art, literature, economics, government, and sociology. The advanced courses, open to juniors and seniors, draw from the same fields.

UNDERGRADUATE COURSE: The senior seminar is being offered for the first time in 1957-58 with a comparison of post-war decades as the subject matter. Pattern and content are to vary from year to year according to the needs and interests of the students. The seminar is directed by members of the history and English departments, with the assistance of other members of participating departments.

COMMENT: The Skidmore program appears to offer a promising method of guiding students toward an understanding of American civilization through a coordinated course program in various traditional departments. The "background" requirement should prevent specialization to the point of parochialism; the advanced course requirements and the senior seminar should encourage a mature understanding of the field, rather than the mere assimilation of information from the related traditional fields.

SMITH COLLEGE, Northampton, Massachusetts.

Daniel Aaron, Director, American Studies.

An American studies major leading to an A. B. degree and including
two courses in American studies.

1939.

Enrollment limited each year to 25 majors.

ADMINISTRATION: This program has an independent director
assisted by a steering committee representing those traditional departments offering courses included in the American studies major.

UNDERGRADUATE PROGRAM: The major consists of an interdepartmental program of courses in history, literature, government,
education, religion, philosophy and art. Students majoring in American
studies are required in their freshman and sophomore years to take the
history of Western civilization and either American literature or a
course which combines American history and the social sciences. In
the junior and senior years, majors must take at least nine hours in
American history and twelve hours in related fields. In addition, juniors
take a required semester course in methodology and seniors take a
second semester course which in some measure integrates other courses
taken as part of the major. The American studies major ranks among
the first five major programs at Smith, although enrollment in the major is limited in number to twenty-five students.

UNDERGRADUATE COURSES: As noted above, there are two
courses required of all American studies majors. The first is required
in the first semester of the junior year. In the words of Donald Sheehan,
who directs it, this course "is designed to suggest the contribution which
the various academic disciplines..., can make to the study of American
culture, conceived as a whole. The contribution of each is conceived
to be of two kinds: subject matter and methodology... The course is
designed fundamentally to make students aware of the interdisciplinary
value of their study and of the vital importance of going beyond a mere
synthesis of subject matter." It is a seminar course given by the director with the assistance of individual instructors from the related disciplines. The second required course, also of seminar nature, is for
seniors in their last semester. As Daniel Aaron describes it, it is
"based on a series of 'classic' texts embracing subjects covered by the
major." The final examination is "based on books studied in the course
but relating also to courses taken in the major during the last two years
and amounts, in effect, to a comprehensive examination."

COMMENT: The Smith program is, of course, "designed for students who have a particular interest in American history and culture," but each student is encouraged to develop a specialized interest within the field so that a superficial program of studies will be avoided. In this connection, it is the hope at Smith that the program will soon be limited to candidates for honors so that a high intellectual standard can be maintained. A distinctive feature of this program is the insistence that each student be thoroughly familiar with the European phases of her particular interest. At the same time, the junior course in American studies makes a greater effort than many similar courses in other institutions to understand American culture as a whole.

SOUTHERN METHODIST UNIVERSITY, Dallas, Texas.

Paul F. Boller, Jr. (history).

Special undergraduate course in American civilization.

1948.

ADMINISTRATION: The course mentioned above is given under the auspices of the history department. Although a program in American studies exists only on paper, there is interest in it on the part of the faculty, at least, and a feeling that a department of American studies would be valid and expedient.

UNDERGRADUATE PROGRAM: The catalogue lists an American civilization major made up of selected courses in the American field; since this major has never been attempted, there is no evidence that it forms a workable curriculum.

UNDERGRADUATE COURSE: The special course in American civilization centers on intellectual history from 17th century Puritanism to the Soviet impact on American thought. Based on such materials as Thorp, Curti, and Baker, American Issues, the Amherst Problems in American Civilization, the work of V. L. Parrington and R. H. Gabriel, the course includes contact with literature, philosophy, religion, as well as history. As an upper class elective, enrollment averages 100 per semester.

COMMENT: Evaluation of activities at Southern Methodist may fairly rest with this statement of the objectives of the course described above: "(1) to give the student some understanding of the ideas and interests that have gone into the molding of the American world view: (2) to show the relationships of the American intellectual heritage to Western civilization; (3) to develop the students' interest in the adventure of ideas."

STATE TEACHERS COLLEGE, Bemidji, Minnesota.

Ruth E. Brune (English), Chairman of American humanities.

An American humanities program leading to the B. S. and including two courses in American humanities.

1950.

20 candidates for the B. S.

ADMINISTRATION: The program at Bemidji has quasi-departmental status with control of curriculum. An independent chairman from the English department directs the program in consultation with a staff committee representing social studies, music, and art. These departments were active in instituting the program. Full departmental status is considered both valid and expedient, so long as courses from traditional departments are included in the program.

UNDERGRADUATE PROGRAM: Freshman-sophomore requirements for the B. S. in American humanities include 12 quarter hours of communication; 9 of world history; 3 of American government; 3 of social studies elective; 12 of science; 6 of physical education; 3 of speech; 3 of general psychology; 1 of library science; 1 of orientation; 3 of music appreciation; 9 of American literature; 3 of American humanities; and 3 of art appreciation. Junior-senior requirements include 12 quarter hours of American history; three of advanced composition or creative writing; four hours seminar in American humanities; and 15 quarter hours of electives from English, social studies, music, art, and speech. English and social studies have proved about equally popular as fields of concentration within the program.

UNDERGRADUATE COURSES: The one-quarter lower division course in American humanities has followed various plans, the most successful being a regional (New England, South, Midwest, and Far West) approach to the history, literature, music, and art of the last 50

- 79 -

to 75 years. The course is taught by an English professor, who calls on specialists (history, music, art) to supplement discussion, panel presentation, and individual student papers. Material for the latter is obtained largely from the library's American humanities shelf of about 50 volumes on history, literature, art, and music.

The upper division seminar is designed to help seniors organize correlated work for teaching. Students are required to do considerable independent research centered on such themes as "the struggle for independence," "the struggle for equality," "the struggle for survival."

COMMENT: The major in American humanities is designed to prepare the student to teach English and social studies or a combination of the two in high school or junior high school, as well as to help him to appreciate the close inter-relationship of various aspects of the American culture. In the question of departmental participation in this program, and in the name chosen for the program, one sees perhaps a special outgrowth of departmental organization in the teachers college where history has been absorbed into the social sciences. Here, perhaps, first steps towards interdisciplinary courses must start with the humanities, on the one hand, and the social sciences on the other. At Bemidji, this bifurcation has been stemmed, at least, by inviting a history professor to lecture in the lower division course. The program is among the last five among majors offered, according to numbers enrolled, but enrollment has grown steadily since the program was instituted; the courses have become increasingly popular as electives. The overwhelming proportion of graduates from the program go into teaching.

STATE TEACHERS COLLEGE, Elizabeth City, North Carolina.

George L. Davis, Dean of the College.

An American civilization program for majors in elementary education.

1937.

264 majors reported.

ADMINISTRATION: The American civilization program at State Teachers College is offered and administered by the social studies department. Separate departmental status for the program is considered valid, and it is possible for an instructor to make a career in American civilization.

UNDERGRADUATE PROGRAM: Majors in elementary education concentrating in American civilization are expected to take three quarters of geography and three quarters of "World Civilization" in their freshman year, three quarters of American history and one quarter of American government in their sophomore year, and one quarter of American literature and a course in the philosophy of education during the final two years. Extensive use is made of films, public lectures, concerts, and student organizations. There is no special course in American civilization.

COMMENT: The American studies program is designed "to influence good, loyal, and active citizenship... pride and appreciation for American ingenuity. To indoctrinate students with the idea of keeping the American heritage secure." Attitude of the faculty to the offerings is mixed. As a result of the program in American studies, courses in "Modern World Politics," "Contemporary Affairs," and "Modern European History" have been added to traditional departments. The idea of using an American studies concentration to supplement an education program is an appealing one; it is disappointingly significant that this program is being used at State Teachers College with prospective elementary rather than secondary teachers and that it seems to emphasize "indoctrination" rather than exploration of subject matter.

STATE UNIVERSITY OF IOWA, Iowa City, Iowa.

A. C. Kern (English), Chairman of the major in American Civilization.

An American civilization program leading to the B. A., including four courses in American civilization; a graduate program leading to the M. A. and the Ph. D., including two courses in American civilization.

Undergraduate program, 1949; graduate program, 1934.

4 undergraduate majors; 2 M. A. candidates; 8 Ph. D. candidates.

ADMINISTRATION: The programs at Iowa have a quasi-departmental status with control of curriculum, administered by a steering committee of representatives from various departments, and directed by an independent chairman who is on the English faculty. Full departmental status for the program is considered neither valid nor expedient.

UNDERGRADUATE PROGRAM: Specific requirements for the B. A. in American civilization are confined to the upper level, as follows: four one-semester courses of history, four of social sciences, two of American literature, two of philosophy and/or fine arts; and two of undergraduate seminars for integration. The program is characterized as an interdepartmental major including humanities, social sciences, and history, and without special concentration of work in any of the traditional fields. As a result of the program, two courses have been added to the offerings of traditional departments: "Significant Books in American Civilization," in the English department; and "History of American Philosophy." The required number of hours has been lowered from 60 to 48 since the program was instituted, but the minimum is still greater than those of traditional majors. Graduates most frequently go into high school teaching; law school, library school, graduate study in the humanities, and government service claim almost equal numbers of those who don't teach.

UNDERGRADUATE COURSES: Two proseminars are taken by majors in the junior and senior years from a rotating sequence: I, "Introduction to American Civilization," deals with selected topics of contemporary society, emphasizing the methodology of the various disciplines. Lectures and discussions are led by specialists in the various fields, and reports by students may be required. II, "The Revolution and Constitution," is concerned with the political thought, the economy, the literature, philosophy, and fine arts of the period. Lectures and discussion are conducted by one professor, and term papers are given as reports. III, "The Age of Jackson," taught in the same way and stressing Tocqueville, transcendentalism, literature, and the arts, has been replaced by "The American Renaissance" with more emphasis on Hawthorne and Melville. IV, "The 1920's" emphasizes the cultural climate, literature, the fine arts, and science and technology; popular optimism and literary pessimism are contrasted. Basic works, such as Parrington and Curti, as well as several literary works, are used in each course, in addition to library materials. The courses are designed as both training for majors and as liberal education offerings providing a new approach to American civilization.

GRADUATE PROGRAM: The graduate student majors in either American literature or American history and spreads the rest of his work in the aforementioned non-major, the social sciences (at least two), the fine arts, philosophy, and European background. About half the work is done in the major area; if history, about 15 hours in literature is required, and vice versa. If English is the elected department, enough English literature for basic teaching purposes is required. Two courses--a seminar in American civilization and "Social Factors in

American Literature"-- have been added to the offerings of history and English departments, respectively, as a result of the program. The chairman of the program feels that courses in American art and (perhaps) in American music would be desirable additional offerings in the traditional departments.

Roughly 80 percent of graduates have majored, as undergraduates, in literature, 20 percent in history, and these proportions have continued to apply to fields of specialization among Ph. D. candidates. Following are some representative Ph. D. thesis topics: "The Psychology of Ernest Hemingway," "The Social Background of Ring Lardner," "Melville and the Quest for God," "Aesthetic Theories of Poe," "The Image of Hollywood in American Fiction," "The Insurgent and Populist Press in the Middle West."

GRADUATE COURSES: No courses are required of all graduate students, but most take both the seminars referred to above. The original American civilization seminar has become the seminar in American intellectual history, employing a standard research topic approach. "Social Factors in American Literature" is a seminar beginning with assumptions and approaches of various disciplines, working in the relations of literature and the arts and of literature and society, as shown by historical, sociological, and anthropological techniques. These seminars regularly attract from eight to ten students outside the American civilization program.

COMMENT: The American civilization program is intended to offer an integrated liberal education which gives the student an opportunity to understand his own culture through analysis and a subsequent synthesis rather than through indoctrination; a historical treatment which will increase the student's comprehension of contemporary institutions and how they can develop consistently with American ideals; and an opportunity for the student to fit himself for intelligent citizenship. Reaction to the program among the University's faculty is mostly favorable, with some pockets of opposition. The graduate program is exceptional in that either of two degrees can be obtained by the Ph. D. candidate: English (American civilization) and history (American civilization). This plan of concentration seems valid, inasmuch as most Ph. D. 's will teach in one of these areas. The popularity of the graduate program, as attested to by enrollment, has increased steadily since the war.

STETSON UNIVERSITY, DeLand, Florida.

John A. Hague, Director, American Studies.

Undergraduate major leading to A. B. degree with special courses. Graduate major leading to the M. A. degree. Special summer program.

1955.

Undergraduate - 4; graduate - 4.

ADMINISTRATION: The department of American studies is an independent department directly under the jurisdiction of the dean of the college of liberal arts. The department has a director who has control over the curriculum and budget. The history department and the college dean were primarily responsible for establishing the American studies program. The program itself was made possible by a grant from the late Charles Merrill. At present it is a one-man department and probably will remain such for at least another three years.

UNDERGRADUATE PROGRAM: In addition to the general education requirements, a major in American studies must complete 6 hours of American history and an introductory course in one of the social sciences as departmental prerequisites. The major program must include 6 hours in American literature, 6 hours in 20th century arts and letters, 3 hours in economic history, 3 hours in American national government, and 3 hours in methods of social research. In addition, the major must complete 3 special courses offered by the director. Enrollment is still very small, although combination majors have been worked out with the division of education and the department of religion.

UNDERGRADUATE COURSES: The first of these is a 6 hour course offered in the junior year which consists of a survey of American intellectual history. Books used in this course include the texts by Gabriel and Parrington and numerous pocket books including Perry Miller's American Puritanism, a Jefferson reader, an Emerson reader, Hofstadter's Social Darwinism and American Political Tradition, Mumford's Brown Decades. The other two courses are senior seminars. The first of these is a study of the American national character in which Tocqueville, Rourke, Turner, Potter, Henry James, Santayana, and Riesman are examined. The second is a seminar dealing with the problems of leadership and social change. In this course the leadership of various movements is examined in an attempt to enable the individual to see himself as a creative force within an evolving culture. Books in this course range from the Lasswell Studies to biographies of individual Americans.

GRADUATE PROGRAM: The requirements for all M. A. degrees at Stetson include 24 hours of courses, a thesis, and an oral examination. These courses consist mainly of seminars offered by the history department and independent reading courses offered by the director of American studies.

The department also offers a 6 hour course in the summer session aimed primarily at high school teachers. In the summer of 1955 a course on communism and democracy was offered. In 1956 the course was "Protestant Heritage of American Thought," in 1957, "Recent Patterns of American Thought," and in 1958, "American National Character." There were 19 students in the seminar in 1956. Although the summer course is not primarily for graduate credit, it may be taken as such.

COMMENT: The American Studies Program is still in its beginning stages. Very rigid requirements have served to keep the number of students down and also to make the program something of an honors program. Most members of the faculty have a favorable attitude toward the department, but few of them are recommending undergraduate majors in American studies. On the other hand, the graduate program now has as many majors as any department outside the division of education.

SWEET BRIAR COLLEGE, Sweet Briar, Virginia.

James A. Rawley (history).

An American civilization major program leading to the B. A. degree.

1955.

3 candidates for the A. B.

ADMINISTRATION: American studies at Sweet Briar is organized as an interdepartmental program under the direction of co-chairmen representing the departments of history and literature. The department of history was most active in instituting the offerings. It is not possible for an instructor to make a career in American civilization at Sweet Briar.

UNDERGRADUATE PROGRAM: There is no special course in American studies. The offering at Sweet Briar is an interdepartmental major in American history and literature, with generous room afforded for related studies. Primary stress is on the interrelationship of history and literature. There are no prerequisites in the freshman and sophomore year. In the junior and senior years four semesters of American literature are required. History and literature are the only fields in which majors are required to take courses. Students majoring in the field are of average ability who enroll primarily out of intellectual curiosity.

COMMENT: The program is a new one and has had only three students in each of the two years in which it has been in operation. However, those in charge of the program feel that if the major is given focus and depth it is as valid as a more limited field, say literature or history alone, and that establishment of a full-fledged department of American studies would be a valid next step. A course on "Religious Groups in the United States" has been added to the curriculum as a result of the program. It is felt that a course in American philosophy is needed to make a balanced program.

SYRACUSE UNIVERSITY, Syracuse, New York.

Stuart Gerry Brown, Chairman, Committee on American Studies.

Undergraduate major program in American studies, including senior seminar required of all majors.

1948.

52 major students.

ADMINISTRATION: The American studies program is administered as a quasi-department with control of its own staff and curriculum. It is directed by a steering committee appointed by the vice-chancellor of the university, who chooses men from the traditional departments who have interest in the program. Instructors are not appointed with the expectation that their career will be wholly in American studies, and the creation of a full-fledged separate American studies department is regarded as neither valid nor expedient.

UNDERGRADUATE PROGRAM: All majors must take a year of American history and a year of American literature in the first two undergraduate years. They must then take other courses in the fields of history, literature, philosophy and any of a number of other American studies fields. The total course requirements of 42 hours are considerably more than the 30 to 36 hours required for majors in the traditional departments.

UNDERGRADUATE COURSES: Major students also take a junior year proseminar in research methods, followed by a senior year seminar in American civilization. Separate sections of the senior seminar are provided for honors and non-honors candidates. The seminar is taught by two professors from different disciplines, one of whom sits at each end of the seminar table. Topics vary from year to year, and involve either a period or a special topic. Seminar meetings feature guided discussion of common reading assignments. Among the books which have been used are Niebuhr's Irony of American History, Riesman's Individualism Reconsidered, and William Allen White's Autobiography. Each seminar student presents one report and prepares a paper.

COMMENT: Syracuse presents a systematic and coordinated approach to the American studies field. The interest developed by the major has led to the establishment of new courses in American art. There is some feeling that a reduction in the number of courses required, if accompanied by an improvement in the quality of courses taken, might improve the program. General faculty attitude is on the whole favorable.

TULANE UNIVERSITY, New Orleans, Louisiana.

W. Burlie Brown.

Special course in American civilization: one of four required in general education of all students. Special summer program for high school teachers.

1951.

ADMINISTRATION: The American studies program at Tulane consists of a special course in American civilization which is offered under the auspices of the history department. A faculty career in American studies is not at present possible.

UNDERGRADUATE COURSE: The course involved is one of four general education courses which are required of all students. It and the general education courses on Western civilization appear to be the most popular of these courses. The special course "aims to provide the student with an introduction to the problem of understanding contemporary American Civilization." Its main approach is historical, although the emphasis is on the contemporary. Attention is given to the agrarian background and the impact of urbanization and industrialization upon American society. In studying urban-industrial society the techno-politico-economic complex, the socio-politico-ethical complex, and the intellectual-emotional complex receive special attention. Finally a lengthy analysis is made of the search for creative expression in an urban-industrial civilization. Students study trends in sculpture, music, literature and the mass media; also architecture and painting. Current enrollment is about 120 students.

A wide variety of materials is used, but special emphasis is given to the Amherst series of Problems in American Civilization. Major books which are also required, include Constance Rourke, Roots of American Culture; John A. Kouwenhoven, Made in America; Lea Gurko, Heroes, Highbrows, and the Popular Mind, and Joseph Wood Krutch, et. al., Is the Common Man Too Common.

COMMENT: The course utilizes a broad range of materials and would seem to offer a competent analysis of American society. The course instructor does not believe that a full-fledged department of American studies would be valid or expedient, and no undergraduate major exists as such. The course is, however, one of the most imaginative of its kind. The history department at Tulane is very progressive and has a strong interest in social, cultural and intellectual history. American studies training will in all likelihood exist entirely within this department. The summer program is one of those sponsored by the Coe Foundation and was first offered in 1957. For a discussion of these programs, see "Summer 'Refresher' Programs," below.

UNION COLLEGE, Schenectady, New York.

Harold A. Larrabee (philosophy), Chairman, Committee on Interdivisional Major in American Studies.

Interdivisional major program in American studies; special course in American studies for engineering students only.

1954.

No undergraduate majors.

ADMINISTRATION: A three-member interdivisional committee, composed of members of the humanities and social studies divisions, directs the major program in American studies. There is no department of American studies, nor do the American studies people at Union regard it as either valid or expedient to establish such a department in a small college such as Union. Under the present arrangement, however, it is possible for a teacher with training in American civilization to make his career in the field, and there is one professor of American civilization.

UNDERGRADUATE PROGRAM: Students who wish to major in American civilization are required to take upper-class courses in American literature and in American social and intellectual history. Beyond this, they must take four courses of one year each chosen from the fields of American history, literature, philosophy, an appropriate departmental seminar course, and a required interdivisional seminar course in American thought.

UNDERGRADUATE COURSE: The interdivisional seminar in American thought, which combines literature and philosophy and which climaxes the major program, has been temporarily supported with funds donated by the Carnegie Corporation. This seminar is not, however, considered as a special American studies offering.

A special course, however, has been developed. It is a full year course required of and limited to engineering seniors. Touching on practically all approaches to the study of American civilization, it stresses literary and historical materials and a method based on selected themes which are treated by the lecture-discussion method under a single faculty member trained in literature and American civilization.

COMMENT: The Union College offerings in American civilization are appropriate to a small institution in which the range of course offerings is relatively small and the course requirements relatively simple. Although the possibility of an interdivisional major program has existed since 1934, there have been very few students subscribing to an American civilization curriculum. Most of the present interest in American studies centers around the required engineering course; good enrollments are reported, however, in courses central to the American field, hence good prospects for future development of the major program.

UNIVERSITY OF BUFFALO, Buffalo, New York.

Lyle Glazier (English), Director of American Studies.

At undergraduate level, a major program including junior and senior
tutorial courses in American Studies; at graduate level, a program
leading to the degree of Master of Arts in American Studies.

1952 (undergraduate); 1954 (graduate).

31 undergraduate majors; none currently enrolled in graduate program.

ADMINISTRATION: The American studies program is administered as a part of the English department at Buffalo. The director is
a member of the English department, but has his full teaching load in
American studies. He is assisted by several members of other traditional departments. The broad basis of the American studies program
is indicated by the fact that members of the history, government,
English, and philosophy departments were active in instituting the offerings, with some participation by psychology, sociology, economics,
geology and geography, dramatics and speech, and art. Both faculty and
administrative attitudes are reported as favorable. No real need of
separate departmental status is seen, although American studies personnel have suggested that quasi-independent status (including control
of budget and curriculum) within the English department might make for
greater convenience of administration.

UNDERGRADUATE PROGRAM: Buffalo has an extremely flexible set of requirements for the American studies work. Broadly speaking a student may select (a) an interdepartmental major; or (b) a major
in English and American studies. In either case, he pursues a coordinated course program which includes work in American history (four
semesters); American literature (four semesters); and American philosophy (one semester). The interdepartmental major student also takes
courses in at least two other American civilization departments; the
major student in English and American studies fulfills, in addition to
the above, the major requirements of the English department.

UNDERGRADUATE COURSES: Each student also takes tutorial
seminar courses in both the junior and senior years. During the junior
year the interdepartmental major student takes a seminar in American
Studies, in which Amherst "problems" are used, in addition to other
classics in American studies or in English and American literature.
The student majoring in English and American studies, on the other
hand, takes a seminar in English and American literature during his

junior year. Members of the English department, some of whom have training especially in American studies, teach these junior tutorial seminars.

During the senior year, a tutorial seminar in music, poetry, and art is taken by both the interdepartmental majors and the English and American studies majors. This seminar is taught by three teachers, one each from the fields of music, poetry, and art.

GRADUATE PROGRAM: A program in American studies leading to the Master of Arts degree is offered. Degree candidates work out special programs with distribution requirements in at least two American studies departments. There is no separate American studies course at the graduate level.

COMMENT: Buffalo personnel regard American studies as a highly eclectic field, comparable as an intellectual discipline to the traditional fields but offering concentration upon the American area rather than upon a department. The program has elicited wide interest and support, and its vitality is suggested by the expansion of older offerings in American intellectual history, and the addition of several new literature courses. The administrative arrangements and emphasis selected by most of the students provide an orientation inclining either toward literature or toward the social sciences. The senior seminar in music, poetry, and art is unusual as a required offering for undergraduate majors in American studies programs. The breadth of the undergraduate program is, at first glance, appalling; a notable success in its execution has been attained, however, by the selection of a number of clear alternatives and through the judicious use of integrating tutorial seminars.

UNIVERSITY OF CALIFORNIA, Berkeley, California.

John Edwards, American Studies Honors Course; Norman Jacobson, American Civilization Group Major.

A. B. Major in American civilization; American Studies Honors Course for sophomores.

Program established, 1941; course established, 1956.

Program -- 1; course -- 45.

ADMINISTRATION: The University of California offers an undergraduate major in American studies and a single "American Studies
Honors Course," the latter established in 1956 on an experimental basis.
The major program is administered by a single "coordinator" who ap-
proves student programs but has no control over faculty, course offerings, or other American studies activities. The "American Studies
Honors Course" is an undertaking of three faculty members in the College of Letters and Sciences, nominally presented as an offering of
three participating departments - - history, English, and political
science. The faculty members involved, representing each of the fields,
both plan and instruct in the course, devoting two-thirds of their teaching time to it. There is no connection, administrative or otherwise,
between the American civilization program and the "American Studies
Honors Course."

UNDERGRADUATE PROGRAM: The program itself only requires
that the student concentrate on American aspects of one of the following
fields: history, political science, economics, English, philosophy, fine
arts. The courses and faculty belong to traditional departments. No
more than two students have been in the program during any of the past
three years. Both students and faculty are obviously properly characterized as "indifferent" to this adjunct of the General Curriculum pattern
which the University accepts for the A. B.

UNDERGRADUATE COURSE: The "American Studies Honors
Course "was experimentally designed to test the value of inter-disciplinary study, to offer sophomore honors students an opportunity to study a
limited body of material intensively, and to explore non-traditional
teaching methods. Students were admitted to the course only with the
permission of the faculty, and of 100 applicants only 45 were chosen on
the basis of their high academic records as freshmen. The course divides its class into three discussion sections of 15 students, each led
through the year by one of the three instructors. At the end of the first
semester, the students are redistributed so that each works under two
faculty members during the year. Occasionally, lectures are presented
to the entire class, and some informal meetings have been held at faculty
homes in the evening. The year's work concentrates on individual
figures arranged in approximately chronological order: the Puritans;
Jefferson, Adams, Hamilton, Madison, Franklin, Tocqueville; Emerson
and Thoreau; Lincoln, Whitman, Calhoun; Peirce, William James,
Santayana, Dewey, Holmes; Melville, Twain, Henry James, Henry
Adams, Eliot. Stress is placed on discussion and on extensive original
research and writing; no grades are given.

COMMENT: An obvious contrast must be drawn between the American studies program and the "American Studies Honors Course." The first is a loose, permissive, inter-departmental combination at the election of the student, and is presumably aimed at a goal of general education in the area of American experience. The other is a carefully designed project with distinct means and intensive interdisciplinary goals. The former exists with a minimum of administrative and faculty organization and has little appeal to students or, apparently, faculty. The latter is a major undertaking of a faculty group and in its initial appearance had more student applicants than it could admit. So far as the course can be evaluated while in progress for the first time, it may be said to be successful both in student and in faculty response to the experimental instructional situation.

UNIVERSITY OF CALIFORNIA, Davis, California.

W. Turrentine Jackson (history), Chairman of the Committee in American Civilization.

American civilization program for the A. B. degree, including two courses in American civilization which may be elected as part of the major. Special tutorial courses are also offered.

1951 (program); 1946 (course).

33 candidates for the A. B.

ADMINISTRATION: The American civilization program has quasi-departmental status with a chairman and an Area Council which acts in an advisory capacity. Its Council members come from the social sciences, literature, history, and natural science. The faculty involved in the program teach in their special fields of preparation, and expect professional advancement through their traditional departments. It may be said, therefore, that the program exists as a pattern of student educational activity, rather than as a pattern of faculty organization and activity. It has been noted by the chairman that while the program has always been given support at the University, faculty attitudes range widely and are, in short, "mixed." He feels that the establishment of a separate administrative group to guide the program has been both expedient and valid.

UNDERGRADUATE PROGRAM: The major in American civilization is "designed to give students an understanding of their own civilization as a living culture. To this end they are directed to investigate its origins; its development; its economic, political, and social institutions; its philosophy; and its intellectual, scientific, and artistic achievements." Since its inauguration, the program has been among the first three liberal arts majors, in terms of the number enrolled in it. Its greatest support has come from women students, with the number of men in the program steadily increasing. Among the features which have attracted students are its character as a liberal arts and as a non-traditional program, the relatively wide choice of elective courses, and the personal attention each student is given by advisers and faculty committees.

Students entering the major must have fulfilled the general college requirements in the lower division and have completed the prerequisites for the upper division courses they plan to take. They are strongly advised to take a course in the history of Western civilization as part of their general education. As majors, they are guided by an adviser and a faculty committee. Thirty-six units are required for the A. B., of which 24 are accounted for in a core curriculum which includes work in American literature, American political theory, American society, and American social, cultural, and economic history. Nine additional units must be taken from a recommended list, which offers ample opportunity for student elective preferences and includes courses in American art, music, literature, drama, anthropology, sociology, geography, political science, psychology, philosophy, and history, A smaller recommended list provides opportunity for the study of Latin-American civilization by students interested in a comparative approach to American experience. It may be noted that, when it began, the program required only that students concentrate their 35 units in three separate fields of American studies. Later, they were urged to include history, a social science, and a humanities field in their group of three. The present arrangement, therefore, is the result of steady tendencies toward a more firmly organized program, and it provides a regular basis for preparing each student in several important areas of American civilization. It may also be observed that under the earlier, more flexible program, the most popular field of concentration was history, with literature and art ranking second and third, respectively.

In their final senior semester, students are required to pass a comprehensive examination to complete the program. They are enrolled in a three-unit course of preparation for this terminal phase of the American civilization program.

UNDERGRADUATE COURSES: Of the three courses designated "American Civilization," only one is a course in the usual sense. This one, "Science and Society," taught by a faculty member in the biological sciences, considers the mutual reactions between science and American society from such diverse sources as Congressional records and dramatic productions. Pre-requisites for this course include three lower division and two upper division courses in the physical and biological sciences. The other two courses offered under the American civilization heading represent the tutorial approach to the problems of the individual student and are designed (in the one case) to augment available catalogue offerings in a needed direction under the supervision of a faculty member from the relevant department, and (in the other case) to prepare the student via reading lists and reports for the comprehensive examination (three hours written, two hours oral) which climaxes his program.

One further course, offered by the history department and titled "Great Issues in American History: Ideas and Interpretation," deserves mention as an American studies course since it is based on the Amherst problems series and covers the many disciplines included therein. This course is required of all American studies majors.

COMMENT: It is interesting that the very large range of freedom originally allowed the student, under faculty guidance, has been somewhat relinquished in the interests of establishing a balanced program for each major candidate. The emphasis upon American experience is still, however, the principal unifying force in the program, and the expansion of offerings in American social and humanistic studies is still continuing vigorously. The program offers an excellent example of an inter-departmental approach to an American civilization curriculum, with clear and energetic administrative guidance, a demonstrable capacity for innovation and variation from traditional course patterns and programming, and a well-conceived effort to establish a pattern of study which will furnish the broad knowledge of American life described in the course goals.

UNIVERSITY OF DAYTON, Dayton, Ohio.

Albert Rose, Chairman, Department of Political Science.

Major program leading to the B. A.

By 1921.

8 majors with political science emphasis; number of American civilization majors with others emphases not reported.

ADMINISTRATION: The report on activities at this institution, having been submitted by the chairman of the political science department, purports to account for only that phase of the major program falling under the jurisdiction of this particular department. Founded by the departments of history, business, education, and political science, the program has, apparently, fallen largely under the influence of political science and is administered by the chairman and staff of that department. Faculty attitude toward the program is reported as mixed; although the program operates within at least three departments, there seems to be no sentiment towards formalizing this interdepartmental potential, and administration is therefore carried out to a large degree by the individual departments concerned.

UNDERGRADUATE PROGRAM: Operating without a special course in American civilization, the program requires at least some work in history, literature, philosophy, religion, political science, and the study of foreign civilizations. Fixed course requirements, at least under the political science emphasis, include state and national government, international relations, constitutional law, and the history of political thought. The pattern for this major rests basically on selected courses dealing with the American area chosen, most commonly, from history and political science offerings. Literature may be substituted for one of these, but the most usual emphasis involves a political science major and a history minor.

COMMENT: To judge from this partial report, the American civilization program operates primarily as training for future lawyers and government personnel. Professor Rose stresses nationalism as a strong motivation for student interest and, in writing of the aims of the program, cites the "almost drastic action required today" in light of America's place in world affairs. This major has achieved some popularity since, counting only those majors with political science concentration, it ranks among the top third of Dayton's thirty-five undergraduate programs.

UNIVERSITY OF ILLINOIS, Urbana, Illinois.

Sherman Paul (English).

An American studies program leading to the B. A. A special course in American civilization separate from the program.

1946.

2 candidates for the B. A.

ADMINISTRATION: The program is sponsored by the humanities division and directed by a steering committee made up of members of the art, literature, and history departments. Since the program itself includes no special courses, committee duties are largely confined to advising students.

UNDERGRADUATE PROGRAM: Requirements for the B. A. in American studies consist, besides the general prerequisites for freshman and sophomore students, of the following courses: 2 semesters in American history, 2 semesters in American literature, 1 semester American art, 1 semester American philosophy, 2 semesters of selected courses from the fields of economics, geography, education, political science and speech. In addition to that, 2 semesters of advanced American history and 2 semesters of advanced American literature are required. As background material European history and literature are also required. This constitutes then an interdepartmental major in the humanities.

UNDERGRADUATE COURSE: "The Growth of American Culture" exists as a special course in American civilization and as a method of answering upper division humanities requirements. It is staffed by instructors in art, literature, and history, who share lecture assignments and who occasionally participate in joint discussions. Materials include Larkin's Art and Life in America and selected primary materials in the three fields represented. From both student and faculty point of view this course has proven popular indeed, and enrollment has increased each year since its inception.

COMMENT: The question of the validity of American studies at Illinois seems to center on the merits of the interdisciplinary approach. Though limited to the humanities, the program has still had difficulties due to insufficient cooperation between departments. However, when the problem has been placed before a small group, as in the case of the course, success has been forthcoming. The opinion has been expressed that more important than an interdisciplinary program is an interdisciplinary attitude on the part of each faculty member.

UNIVERSITY OF KANSAS, Lawrence, Kansas.

Edward F. Grier, Chairman, American Civilization Program. (Ward L. Miner, Acting Chairman, 1956-57.)

An American civilization program leading to the B. A. and including one course in American civilization.

1953.

10 undergraduate majors in American Civilization.

ADMINISTRATION: The American civilization program at Kansas has a quasi-departmental status with control of curriculum, administered by a steering committee selected among Americanists in various departments, and directed by a chairman trained in American civilization and attached to the English department. Full departmental status for the program is considered valid but inexpedient. Under the present administrative setup, cooperation has been achieved between several departments, and an impressive growth has taken place.

UNDERGRADUATE PROGRAM: Requirements for the B. A. in American civilization include one semester of American history and one semester of an optional social science course (before the end of the junior year), two semesters of American literature, one course in a foreign civilization, and two semesters of American civilization. In addition to these specific course requirements, majors are expected to do work in such fields as: political science, history of art, anthropology, and geography. In the order of their popularity, students usually concentrate, within the American civilization program, in literature, history, and political science. The chairman is of the opinion that additional courses are needed in the fields of music and philosophy. Ranking only among the first twenty in popularity as an undergraduate major, the American civilization enrollment has grown from two to ten in the last four years. Although no specific grade average is required of these majors, they do represent above average students. An unusual aspect of the program was its use of films to attract attention to it at the outset.

UNDERGRADUATE COURSE: A full year senior course in American civilization is required of all majors; either term of the course is offered as an elective to the undergraduate interested in liberal education. The text is Potter, Manning, and Davies, Nationalism and Sectionalism in America (first term) and Government and the American Economy (second term); widely scattered collateral reading is assigned for discussion sessions led by the instructor, a member of the English department. Faculty participation representing the departments of art and social science has also been taken advantage of, and the following fields of knowledge are dealt with: art, architecture, history, literature, philosophy, and religion. The course has not proven popular as an elective.

COMMENT: The American civilization program is offered with the conviction that it allows a better approach to a liberal education than can be obtained in any traditional program. General faculty attitude toward this program is described as indifferent, although the increased enrollment is attributed in part to increased attention paid to it by faculty advisers. In keeping with its rather general objective, this program has kept itself loose and formless as far as general requirements are concerned; hence, the value for the individual student would depend on the perceptiveness of his advisor and the richness of the catalogue for a particular term. Aside from this, the program has no notable characteristics, other than the commendable one of insisting that the student devote at least some time to the study of a foreign civilization. Post-graduate choices of American civilization majors have centered on graduate study in traditional programs or in such professional colleges as law and medicine.

UNIVERSITY OF KANSAS CITY, Kansas City, Missouri. *

John Barnett, Dean, College of Arts and Sciences.

Undergraduate program including some special course offerings; graduate program leading to the M. A.

1940.

3 undergraduate majors; no graduate students.

ADMINISTRATION: Initiated by the departments of history and literature, this program was for some time carried out by these established departments without special administrative apparatus. Recently, however, an interdepartmental committee has been named to exercise supervision.

UNDERGRADUATE PROGRAM: After a long period of operation as a permissive program tailored to individual student interests, Kansas City has this year defined a curriculum based on core courses in art

- 99 -

24705

(6 hours), history and government (12), literature (6), and "Special Readings" (3). A special philosophy course is a virtual requirement, thus adding a fourth field to the student's experience. By requiring a grade average slightly above the university minimum, this program has assumed something of the flavor of an honors curriculum.

UNDERGRADUATE COURSES: The "Special Readings" course listed above has just been introduced as a special feature of the program; however, because of its newness, detailed information is lacking as to its content. A special American studies seminar is also contemplated for the future. In addition to these offerings, two courses from traditional settings have had special relevance to this program: a history course in "American Culture" provides heavy emphasis on art and literature as well as on the usual subjects; a philosophy course called "American Ideals" also has obvious relevance to the program.

GRADUATE PROGRAM: An M. A. in "American Culture" can be achieved by pursuing a schedule of courses selected for the individual student and drawn principally from the areas of literature and history. The course load is slightly heavier than in traditional departments, but no special American studies courses are provided.

COMMENT: The graduate program at Kansas City has had no takers, reportedly, for the last decade and shows no signs of reviving. During a comparable period, there had only been one undergraduate student majoring in American culture. With the appointment of a supervisory committee and with the establishment of a fixed curriculum, the undergraduate program has this year attracted three students and may be on the road to becoming an active program.

UNIVERSITY OF MARYLAND: College Park, Maryland.

Otho T. Beall (English), Executive Secretary, American Civilization Program.

An American civilization program leading to the B. A., M. A., and Ph. D. A special course in American civilization is offered to upperclassmen and graduate students.

1945 (undergraduate and graduate).

Undergraduate 15; M. A. 16; Ph. D. 5.

ADMINISTRATION: The American civilization program at Maryland was initiated by and is conducted within the department of English, and is directed by a steering committee on which are representatives of the various traditional departments. Full departmental status is not considered valid.

UNDERGRADUATE PROGRAM: The major in American civilization is an interdepartmental one in which students follow standard College of Arts and Sciences' prerequisites and choose courses from the departments of English, government and politics, history, and sociology, concentrating in one of these. Upperclassmen are required to take the "Conference Course in American Civilization" (see below). The number of major students in American civilization has averaged about ten per year over the past few years of which about twenty per cent have been foreign students. It is felt that courses in social history and history of science might profitably be added to traditional departments to give balance to the present offerings in American civilization.

UNDERGRADUATE COURSE: The "Conference Course in American Civilization" is organized as a great books course, with lectures given by various specialists. Students are required to read eight books: Franklin's Autobiography, Tocqueville's Democracy in America, Schlesinger's Age of Jackson, Thoreau's Walden, Howells' Rise of Silas Lapham, the Lynds' Middletown, Veblen's Theory of the Leisure Class, and Rose's The Negro in America. Art, architecture, history, literature, and religion are subjects included in the make-up of the course, which has been popular as an elective, especially with science and education majors.

GRADUATE PROGRAM: The degree of Master of Arts in American Civilization is offered cooperatively by the departments of English, government and politics, history, and sociology. Candidates for the degree are supervised by an advisory committee made up of advisers designated by each department, with the chairman of the committee being drawn from the department whose subject the student plans to emphasize. A reading knowledge of one foreign language, preferably French or German, is required as is a minimum of 24 semester hours course work, exclusive of thesis and research. Fifteen hours must be in the field of American studies as offered in any two of the four cooperating departments; normally, one of the two departments will be either history or English. Supporting courses may be chosen from related fields in such a way that the candidate will have the foundation for a sound understanding of American culture. Each candidate for the M. A. degree is required to take the course in bibliography and research methods given by the department whose subject the student emphasizes.

A thesis is required of all candidates who take the 24-semester-hour program; with the approval of the candidate's advisory committee, however, six additional hours of course work may be substituted for the thesis. If such a program is followed the candidate must submit to his advisory committee two substantial seminar papers which he has written. A four-hour written examination, general in scope, is required of all candidates. In addition, an oral examination is given which emphasizes the candidate's research and materials studied in related courses. About sixty per cent of the graduate students in American civilization tend to have concentrated in literature as undergraduates, thirty per cent in history, five per cent in political science, and five per cent in sociology. In their graduate work they tend to concentrate in equivalent proportions in the same fields.

Direction of doctoral work in American civilization is in the hands of an advisory committee designated by the various departments, with the chairman of the committee being drawn from the department whose subject the student plans to emphasize. The equivalent of three years of full time graduate study and research (60 hours of course work plus 12 for the dissertation plus a reading knowledge of two languages) is the minimum required. As soon as the student feels adequately prepared in one interdisciplinary topic, he may apply for permission to take the preliminary, exploratory oral examination, which is approximately one and one-half hours in length. Having satisfactorily passed this examination the candidate must complete a dissertation under the direction of his advisory committee. If the dissertation satisfies the committee, the candidate is given a final written comprehensive examination lasting two and one-half days (six hours per day) in several generally related aspects of American civilization. A final oral examination, three hours in length and dealing mainly with the candidate's dissertation and related subject matter, is also required. The great majority of the dissertations are in the field of American literature. Holders of the Ph. D. degree tend to gravitate principally into literature departments of colleges and universities. Very few are now teaching, even part-time, in American studies.

COMMENT: The aims of the undergraduate program emphasize preparation for living through the study of one's own civilization, yet the program at all levels does little to formalize the curriculum in any fixed direction. The burden of integrating knowledge resulting from this wide choice of course work falls, then, on the student and his advisor(s). To avoid detrimental diffusion of emphasis, it should be noted, students at all levels are required to concentrate their efforts in one of the traditional departments within the scope of the program; and, it should also be noted, the English department has made its influence strongly felt as represented in background, interest, and career of the typical student.

UNIVERSITY OF MIAMI, Coral Gables, Florida.

George K. Smart, Chairman, Committee on American Civilization Curriculum.

Undergraduate major leading to A. B. degree.

1950.

26 candidates for the A. B.

ADMINISTRATION: At the University of Miami there is a committee on American civilization which functions as a quasi-department with control of the curriculum. The history, English, government, and art departments have been instrumental in creating the program which has been favorably received by the faculty. It is possible for an instructor or assistant professor to make a career in American civilization, although it would appear that all such instructors would have to have an affiliation with a traditional department. The chairman of the American civilization committee does not believe that a full-fledged department of American studies would be of value or expedient at the present time.

UNDERGRADUATE PROGRAM: The undergraduate program places its emphasis on liberal education and on the training of students for such specific fields as teaching, government service, and the law. "Each student's program is planned with one of these objectives in mind." In order to qualify for the program, undergraduates must complete in their freshman and sophomore years a two-semester course in American government and eighteen semester hours of work in American history and American literature. There are no special courses required of all students participating in the major program, although a course in social and intellectual history is strongly recommended -- virtually required. The program does not require a concentration of work in any one traditional field, but every program contains "the usual minor requirements." Enrollment has grown from two in 1951, to eleven in 1953, to seventeen in 1954, and to its present size of 26.

COMMENT: The American studies program at the University of Miami seems to be primarily a service department for students with special interests or vocations. The curriculum does not appear to have been modified in any significant way by the creation of a department of American studies. Furthermore, it is interesting to note that in spite of the minimal control which seems to be exercised over the students in this program, the only modification in the program since its inception took the form of revising requirements in the direction of increased flexibility. Thus, from practice, the theory emerges that a "program" in American civilization can exist for only one student at a time, that this "program" must be revised for each individual case, and that it can be adequately outlined from existing traditional courses.

UNIVERSITY OF MICHIGAN, Ann Arbor, Michigan.

Joe Lee Davis (English).

American Culture program leading to the B. A. and including one special course; two American civilization courses for foreign students; course of study leading to the M. A. and Ph. D. degrees offered by special arrangement.

Undergraduate, 1950; graduate, 1948.

10 undergraduate majors; no graduate students.

ADMINISTRATION: The program at Michigan is administered by an interdepartmental steering committee working with the traditional departments; the history and English departments were active in instituting the program. Departmental status is considered both invalid and inexpedient.

UNDERGRADUATE PROGRAM: Freshman-sophomore prerequisites for a major in the program are six semester hours of American history and six semester hours from any two of these departments: English, philosophy, and fine arts. In the upper division, the only specific requirement is a one-semester seminar, "Conference on American Culture," taken in the senior year. The character of the program is best described as an interdepartmental major including humanities, social sciences, and history, without concentration in any single traditional field. Specifically, majors are required to take courses in art, literature, history, philosophy, and the social sciences. The required credit load is somewhat more than that of majors in traditional departments. In number of students enrolled, the program ranks among the last five. Although a specified grade average is not required, students electing the program rank above the University average in intellectual ability.

UNDERGRADUATE COURSE: "Conference on American Culture," required of all seniors in the program, is conducted along seminar lines with enrollment limited to twelve. (Advanced students not in the program may register with permission.) It attempts an evaluation of widely read or popular books in the various fields of American studies, such as Guthrie's The Way West, Hofstadter's The American Political Tradition, Rourke's American Humor, Riesman's The Lonely Crowd. Discussions led by the director of the course, by invited specialists, and by individual students constitute the method. The course deals with both the past and the present and draws upon all of the following disciplines: art, architecture, history, history of science and technology, literature, music, philosophy, and religion. It has so far been conducted by Professor Davis, but will be taught after 1958 by Professor Howard H. Peckham of the department of history and Director of the William L. Clements Library.

Two other courses, under the special charge of Professor Felheim and Dr. Howes, are offered by the program, but for foreign students at the University rather than for majors in the program. Through lectures and discussion-recitation sections, one of these courses deals with the geography and history of the United States, various social, political and economic aspects of its society, and its relations with other countries. The second course consists of readings in ten major American writers.

GRADUATE PROGRAM: There is no regular graduate program or course; instead, the program of the candidate is tailored to his particular interests (most often these have been in history and literature). Under such special arrangements, usually involving a relatively high minimum credit load, two masters and six doctoral degrees have been granted in the past. Anticipated revisions in this curriculum call for a requirement of one-fourth of the student's course work in a culture other than that of the United States.

COMMENT: The steering committee regards the program as "objective, critical, exploratory, and humanistic," designed "to avoid both propaganda and pedantry." Faculty reaction to the program is reported to be favorable. A distinctive characteristic of the program is its "side line" responsibility for providing a broad, liberal education in American civilization and literature for approximately 1,000 foreign students on the campus.

UNIVERSITY OF MINNESOTA, Minneapolis, Minnesota.

Tremaine McDowell (English), chairman of the program in American
    Studies.

An American studies program leading to the B. A. and including three courses; graduate programs leading to the M. A. and Ph. D., each of which includes a seminar.

The undergraduate and M. A. programs in 1945, the Ph. D. program in 1946.

16 undergraduate majors; 18 M. A. candidates; 52 Ph. D. candidates (including those engaged in doctoral dissertations but not on this campus).

ADMINISTRATION: The offerings at Minnesota are administered as an interdepartmental program. The chairman, who is a member of the English faculty, consults with a steering committee representative of departments cooperating in the program. The departments of English, history, sociology, political science, art, and philosophy were active in instituting offerings in the program.

Funds obtained outside the University have been used primarily to give the Minnesota faculty experience in interdisciplinary research and to enrich the summer offerings of traditional departments. Thus, a faculty research seminar in 1955-56 was supported entirely by outside funds; similarly, outside funds support a program of guest professors teaching American courses in traditional departments in the summer sessions from 1955 to 1958, and such funds were used to bring in a visiting lecturer during the first half of 1955-56.

UNDERGRADUATE PROGRAM: The undergraduate program is an interdepartmental major including humanities, social sciences, and history. Freshman-sophomore requirements for a major are three quarters of American life or American humanities, both conducted by the program in American Studies. All upper division students are required to take nine to twelve quarter credits in each of these fields: history of the United States, American literature, American philosophy and fine arts, and the United States in the social sciences. In addition, fifteen quarter credits in a foreign civilization are required. As a result of the program, courses in American philosophy and in American music have been added to traditional departments. Other additions which the program's chairman feels would be desirable are history of science and technology in the United States and history of religion in the United States. Graduates of the program are now employed in journalism, library work, teaching, government service, social work, and miscellaneous positions in business.

UNDERGRADUATE COURSES: The program offers three undergraduate courses: "American Life," "American Humanities," and "Proseminar in American Studies."

"American Life," a freshman-sophomore course, is organized to deal with eight topics arranged with some attention to chronology. Materials include readings in primary sources in American history, literature, social sciences, and philosophy; color slides of American painting, sculpture, and architecture; recordings of American music; films. Lectures by various specialists were tried but abandoned in favor of lectures by a broadly oriented instructor in order to present a better integrated overview of American civilization. A larger proportion of time is devoted to discussion than is true in most departmental courses.

"American Humanities," for juniors and seniors who have not taken "American Life," deals with three topics and employs the same types of materials as does "American Life." Here, too, the method combines extensive discussion with lectures by a single instructor.

The proseminar is taken by seniors majoring in American studies. The course is organized around a theme, and five or six classic works in American civilization are studied intensively each quarter. Discussion is led by a single instructor.

GRADUATE PROGRAM: Both the M. A. and Ph. D. programs are interdisciplinary majors which include humanities, history, and the social sciences. Specifically, masters candidates take equal amounts of work in history, literature, the social sciences, and philosophy and art. Doctoral candidates take, in addition to these, equal work in a foreign civilization -- it may be in more than one civilization and in more than one department, but some pattern must govern such choice. Each candidate's program must deal with American experience in terms of the present and the past.

Most doctoral candidates who have not taken the M. A. are persuaded to take it in an established department -- selecting courses acceptable for the American studies doctorate -- in order that they may have a sound knowledge of one discipline and a disciplinary degree for potential disciplinary employers. Doctoral candidates are required to study ten classic books in American civilization, on which they are examined (in addition to their course work) in the preliminary examination. The preliminary written examination for the doctorate is conducted in five three-hour sessions corresponding to the five fields mentioned above. In the first part of each examination, the candidate is asked to relate materials within that field; in the second part, he is asked to relate materials in that field to materials in other fields. There is also a preliminary oral examination. The final oral examination for the Ph. D. is moving away from more or less casual questioning on the dissertation and the candidate's general knowledge of American civilization toward an incisive examination of the methodologies employed in the dissertation and their relation to American studies. The dissertation itself must involve several disciplines.

GRADUATE COURSES: Three three-quarter courses are offered in the program. The first quarter of the first of these sequences is for M. A. candidates and for Ph. D. candidates who do not have the masters degree in American studies. Aims and methods of the disciplines most relevant to American studies are examined. The second and third quarters of this sequence are for M. A. candidates only; the second provides intensive study of five or six classic works in American civilization; the third is concerned with the theme of religion in American civilization.

A three-quarter seminar is required of Ph. D. candidates. The first quarter is concerned with bibliographical problems in various disciplines. The second and third quarters require individual research and papers on themes related to agrarianism and urbanization, respectively. Each of these graduate courses is conducted by a single instructor.

Another three-quarter seminar, offered for the first time in 1957-58, dealt with original documents for the study of American civilization in the fields of art and architecture, music, philosophy, literature, history, and the social sciences.

COMMENT: The undergraduate program is designed to fulfill two purposes: to bring undergraduates to some understanding of the relationship between the areas of knowledge now segregated within individual departments, and to acquaint students with American civilization per se. "American Life" and "American Humanities" have proved to be popular electives for students not majoring in the program; the four sections of "American Life," for example, are closed at 60, and more would enroll if they could. Particularly gratifying is the diversity of the students' interests -- they come from numerous departments in the arts college and from various professional schools. Faculty reaction at the University is predominantly favorable. The program's chairman feels that operation as an interdepartmental program rather than as a department limits hostility to a minimum.

Twenty-seven doctorates have been granted in the program in the last five years. Of the men to whom these were granted, ten are now teaching at least part-time in American studies. Others teach in English, sociology, history, general studies, and journalism departments, or are engaged in government service and as directors of libraries. Response to a questionnaire circulated among those holding the M. A. and the Ph. D. degrees may be summarized as follows: Teachers who handle introductory departmental courses in American literature, history, and the social sciences find their training relevant and adequate. Teachers who conduct a general course in the humanities or in the social sciences report that interdisciplinary study of American civilization is very useful, even though the materials of their courses are frequently European. After conversations with college administrators and with former students now conducting such courses, the chairman of the program is convinced that until the Ph. D. is granted in the humanities as a whole and in the social sciences as a whole, there is no better preparation than American studies for teaching general courses in these two areas. He is also convinced that an increasing number of graduates will be employed in American studies.

UNIVERSITY OF NEW HAMPSHIRE, Durham, New Hampshire.

Edward Y. Blewett, Dean, College of Liberal Arts.

No degree programs are offered; one course, however, is open to seniors in the college of liberal arts.

1951.

ADMINISTRATION: The American civilization course is administered by a committee of faculty members from the liberal arts faculty. In 1957, for example, it was handled by representatives of education, psychology, and language. The dean of the liberal arts college is adviser to this committee.

The actual teaching of the course is done by members of a much larger group of departments, however. In fact, one of the distinguishing features of the movement to establish the New Hampshire course was the desire to include the physical and biological sciences as well as the social studies and humanities. Thus the departments represented include education, psychology, language, music, speech, art, zoology, geology, philosophy, sociology, economics, government, history, and English.

UNDERGRADUATE COURSE: New Hampshire's course in American civilization has the title, "American Civilization in Transition." It is described as a "senior synthesis" course and its purpose is to provoke mature thinking about America's role in the twentieth-century world. The organization and procedure of the course are designed to cut across departmental lines and to permit each senior, at the climax of his college career, to transcend the boundaries of his major field in considering his own civilization.

Each participating faculty member presents one Monday evening lecture on his own field and the light which it sheds upon American civilization. Thus a sociologist discusses the urban factor in American civilization, a historian discusses the role of the frontier, a professor of government interprets the changing constitution, and a geologist explores the conservation of natural resources as a critical problem in America today.

Before each lecture, the students meet in small sections led by student leaders to discuss reading selections assigned by the professor for his topic. Another round of section meetings is held after the class, to discuss the readings again -- this time in the light of the lecture presentation.

COMMENT: The chief limitation of the New Hampshire course would seem to be the brief consideration of each topic taken up and the difficulty of providing continuity during the year. The chief merit would be the scope of fields and points of view represented. The discussion sessions both before and after the lectures serve to make the students more than passive listeners. This course has proven exceptionally popular with the students, having filled its limited enrollment each semester it has been offered. The limit has been increased from one section of thirty to three sections of thirty each, totalling ninety in the lecture meetings.

UNIVERSITY OF NEW MEXICO, Albuquerque, New Mexico.

George Arms (English).

No undergraduate activity; program leading to the Ph. D. including one course in American Civilization. (For further details see American Studies, I [April, 1956], 1-2, 4.)

1944.

10 candidates for the Ph. D.

ADMINISTRATION: The program is administered by a steering committee composed of representatives of their fields of learning who also represent the principal cooperating departments. At present this committee is composed of two members each from history, literature, and the social sciences. The chairman of this committee also serves, to some degree, as an independent director. The present administrative status is considered satisfactory by those involved, and there is no pressure for departmental autonomy.

GRADUATE PROGRAM: This is strictly a doctoral program, and entering students are presupposed to have an M. A. in such fields as history, English, education, sociology, political science, philosophy, and economics. Considering the varieties of backgrounds and objectives among their students, as well as the variations in course offerings, the persons responsible for American studies at New Mexico have attempted to write a large degree of flexibility into their program. Considerable individual attention is given each student in the form of a special reading list, for example, and in the form of a special committee appointed by the permanent Committee on Studies to oversee the program of each student. The candidate's work culminates in three examinations: a preliminary oral, a written, and a final oral dealing mainly with the dissertation and its related fields. Among other subjects, the candidate is examined in his choice of four out of six areas of American language and literature, and two out of three periods of American history. Other departments in which the student may elect courses concerned with American culture are: art, economics, education, government, music, philosophy, sociology, and speech. (In art, education, and speech, the approved courses are historical or philosophical in their approach.) Course offerings include such relatively uncommon titles as: "The Folk Tale in English," "American Language Seminar," "Contemporary Musical Literature," "Composers of the United States," "Periods of Special Philosophical Significance," "Philosophy of Art Education," and "American Public Address." The student is thought of as developing his background in three principal areas: (1) American literature, fine arts, and philosophy; (2) American history and education; and (3) American social thought and institutions. A typical course of study would be drawn from the following fields (number of courses offered in parentheses): American literature (11), fine arts (3), philosophy (6), history (18), education (4), social thought and institutions (24). An exceptional aspect of this program would appear to be the degree of correlation possible between the American studies program and such fields as music and education. Research assets include relatively strong holdings in American language and literature (especially regional), American history (especially the 19th century), and certain branches of the social sciences.

GRADUATE COURSE: A minimum of one interdepartmental seminar in American civilization is required of all doctoral candidates. Taught by members of the English, history, or sociology departments, these seminars have been unified by various themes (i. e., America from 1700-1830 as seen through reports of travelers; or, religious backgrounds in America during the 19th century). Each week a particular topic is chosen and outlined; the session is opened by a lecture from one of the staff or from a visiting specialist, after which discussion takes place. The materials, of course, vary from year to year, but tend to represent most of the major relevant areas of learning.

COMMENT: After a slow start (only three degrees were awarded in the first twelve years of the program's existence), recent years have shown a marked increase in enrollment, perhaps partially due to the establishment in 1954 of the graduate seminar which now annually attracts from nine to twelve students including some 30% from outside the program. Criticism of the program has been met by a tightening of its definition and practice, and by a careful screening and supervising of candidates. Students are chosen from among those of above average abilities and of definite and direct interest in utilizing the peculiar advantages of the program. Entering students have their training in literature (about one-third), history (about one-third), and other fields (including political science, religion, and education). While pursuing the program, they tend to specialize in history (about 70%) and literature (about 30%). Of the three who have completed their doctorates, however, two are teaching literature and one is a college dean.

UNIVERSITY OF PENNSYLVANIA, Philadelphia, Pennsylvania.

Robert E. Spiller (English), Chairman, American Civilization Department.

Degree programs leading to the B. A., M. A., and Ph. D. Special American civilization courses as follows: two undergraduate; one open to undergraduates and graduates; one special summer course; one graduate seminar; and one faculty-graduate student seminar.

Graduate, 1938; undergraduate, 1942.

30 candidates for the B. A.; 20 candidates for the M. A.; and 51 candidates for the Ph. D.

ADMINISTRATION: The program is actually administered by a committee appointed by the deans of the college and the graduate school, but for budgetary purposes it is considered to be a separate department. The chairmanship is rotating and is usually held by a member of either the history or the literature department. At present the department has a grant from the Carnegie Foundation amounting to $30,000 per year until 1960. Regular teaching however is on the University budget. The grant is used chiefly to finance a visiting lectureship, a series of post-doctoral fellowships, and for scholarship and fellowship purposes. It is possible to make a career in American civilization at the University of Pennsylvania, and two men in the department now hold appointments in American civilization. The program was founded by history and literature with aid from political science, and now has the cooperation of a number of other departments.

UNDERGRADUATE PROGRAM: This program is organized around two courses in American civilization, one at the junior and one at the senior level. Although there are no fixed major requirements aside from these two courses, there are a number of courses considered to be major-related (including courses in art, music, philosophy, religion, political science, sociology, geography, economics) and students are expected to take work in American literature and history. The informal nature of the major, of course, puts the onus completely on the student's advisor. After a slow beginning, the program has risen to a place among the first ten majors in the college.

UNDERGRADUATE COURSES: There are two such in the regular year. The junior course -- American Civilization 1 -- is a course in American culture from 1650 to 1950, using the culture concept as an integrating device applied to primary materials from the society. Its enrollment has risen steadily from four or five in its first years to forty-two this year. The second course, American Civilization 300, is a senior conference course organized on a thematic basis. Accordingly it is narrower yet more intensive than AC 1. Some use has been made of the Amherst series, yet here too the emphasis has been on original materials. In addition to these two courses, there are two others now active which are open to both graduate and undergraduate students. One is a lecture course during the regular year dealing with the impact of science on American culture; the orientation is cultural, employing the culture concept. The other is a summer workshop dealing with urban culture and utilizing the facilities of the Philadelphia area as well as of the University. In this category of graduate-undergraduate course, a one-term course called "American Forms and Values" had been offered by Lewis Mumford, but has now been discontinued.

GRADUATE PROGRAM: The graduate program is organized in the same way as the undergraduate, with a central core of American civilization courses and a group of traditional courses in other departments. These courses are in the departments of art, architecture, history, literature, music, philosophy, religious thought, sociology, anthropology, political science, economics, psychology. The student must stand on his preliminary for three fields -- history, either literature or art, and one other. History and literature continue to dominate the program although other subjects play an ever increasing role.

GRADUATE COURSES: A seminar in methods and research, operating for the full year, is required of graduate students, regardless of their level of advancement, during the first year of residence. The course culminates in a thesis which fulfills the thesis requirement for the M. A. The staff for this course varies from year to year and often includes visits by various faculty members covering their respective fields of interest. The question of methods and approaches to the study of civilization is favored at the expense of coverage of specific materials. Beginning in 1954, a faculty-graduate student seminar has met for the consideration of special problems in the field, such as methods of relating the historical and social scientific approach to the question of social values.

COMMENT: The program at Pennsylvania has obviously been unusually successful. Its objectives have been both to provide a more liberal education and to create a new approach to the study of American life, and for this purpose it has made rather extensive use of the culture concept. It would not be true to say that the cultural point of view dominates the program in any sense; thematic, institutional, and traditional approaches play too essential a role. But the program has gone farther toward the development of a discipline of American civilization than most.

UNIVERSITY OF ROCHESTER, Rochester 20, New York.

Margaret Denny (English).

Major program including integrating seminar.

1952.

One undergraduate major.

ADMINISTRATION: The American studies major at Rochester is directed by a steering committee of representatives of traditional departments. The program has quasi-departmental status with control of curriculum. Members of the English department have been primarily involved in the program, with varying degrees of participation by the departments of history, economics, sociology, art, geography, and philosophy. It is not possible for a teacher to make a career exclusively in American studies, and much of the participation has been extra work, over and above a full load in a traditional department, without extra credit or compensation.

UNDERGRADUATE PROGRAM: American studies majors take a course load of 42 hours in the major (the usual requirement for a departmental major is 36 hours). Courses in American history, economic history, and government must be taken, plus a minimum of nine hours in American art, literature, and philosophy. Courses in sociology and education may also be counted toward the American studies major.

UNDERGRADUATE COURSE: An integrating seminar must be taken during the junior and senior years. The seminar meets once per week, and carries three hours credit per year. Juniors and seniors participate together in the seminar. The seminar is designed to integrate work in other courses rather than to impart new information. The emphasis is upon native (especially the frontier) and foreign influences upon American life.

COMMENT: The program at Rochester has sought to encourage a comprehensive analysis of, and understanding of, the forces underlying American history, economics, and literature. It has a sensibly planned combination of traditional course requirements and integrating work in American studies. It has suffered from lack of personnel with primary training in, and responsibility for, American studies, and also from a generally indifferent attitude toward the program by members of the faculty and administration. The effect of this indifference has caused a prediction that both course and program will be abandoned as of June, 1958.

UNIVERSITY OF SOUTHERN CALIFORNIA, Los Angeles, California.

Russell L. Caldwell, Chairman, Department of General Studies in American Civilization and Institutions.

Required American Civilization course.

1946.

ADMINISTRATION: The 5-unit, required general education course in "American Civilization and Institutions" is administered by a chairman under the authority of the Dean of Liberal Arts and Sciences. It is taught by a staff of three faculty members (including the chairman) and a group of graduate assistants who lead voluntary "Preceptorial Sections." It is not part of any departmental major in the social sciences, and its faculty divide their efforts between this general education course and instruction in typical department fields of the social sciences. They depend on the latter for professional advancement.

UNDERGRADUATE COURSE: The course is designed to present the principal features of American historical development, considering such major episodes and themes as the Westward movement, for example, and examining the growth of political, socio-economic, and cultural institutions in America.

COMMENT: The course undertakes its synthesis of materials in terms of "Concepts and Great Generalizations" in American culture, as a basis for understanding the cultural progress of the American people. It represents, in a general way, the not uncommon response of California colleges and universities to the State requirement that teacher-candidates and graduates of publicly-supported institutions receive instruction in American national, state, and local history and government.

UNIVERSITY OF TENNESSEE, Knoxville, Tennessee.

LeRoy P. Graf (history), Chairman of American Civilization Committee, and Adviser to Majors.

An interdepartmental major program in American civilization leading to the B. A. degree.

1949.

ADMINISTRATION: The American civilization program at Tennessee is directed by a steering committee consisting of representatives from the departments of history, political science, sociology, philosophy, economics, and English. The chairman (a member of the history department) handles the administrative details. Although the principal initiative in the creation of the program was given by the history and English departments, the departments of economics, sociology, philosophy, and political science cooperated in its organization. Separate departmental status for the program is not considered valid or expedient.

UNDERGRADUATE PROGRAM: The American civilization program is an interdepartmental major in the College of Liberal Arts. The major consists of forty-five quarter hours, of which thirty must be devoted to required courses while the other fifteen hours may be elected from a wide range of subjects in the fields of English, fine arts, philosophy, economics, history, political science, sociology, journalism, and geography. Courses required for the major include a one-year American history survey, a one-year American literature survey, one quarter of American philosophy, one year of American government, and two quarters of sociology -- one dealing with urban problems and the other with minority groups. Foreign civilization is not studied as part of the major but as part of the College of Liberal Arts' requirement of a foreign language and survey of European history. Majors have tended to concentrate (through their minors) on literature, history, and sociology, in that order.

COMMENT: The American civilization program attempts to provide students with the opportunity of taking courses in a variety of departments and yet of having the unifying factor of focus upon the American experience. The attitude of the staff handling the program and the faculty as a whole is favorable. It is felt that the major is a valid approach toward a liberal education and a good background for teaching, law, journalism, business, government and diplomatic service, and other areas in which human relations are important. Though more hours are required than in the traditional major, this is offset by the fact that several of these hours can also be used in meeting the general requirements of the College of Liberal Arts. A variety of obstacles has prevented the introduction of a special course in American civilization, but it is hoped that it will eventually be created. In the years following the establishment of the major there was a steady increase in major students from six to eleven. At the present time, however, the number is six.

UNIVERSITY OF UTAH, Salt Lake City, Utah.

William Mulder (English), Director, American Studies Institute.

Program leading to doctorate in one of the traditional humanities departments may be supplemented by work in American studies, including a course on the graduate level. For other activities, see below.

1953.

4 candidates for the Ph. D. in English are taking the American studies curriculum.

ADMINISTRATION: To supplement American studies activities, an Institute of American Studies was established in May, 1956. The purpose of the Institute is to promote the exploration of interdepartmental relationships involving American culture; to do this, it relies on a program of publication including The Western Humanities Review; the sponsorship of extracurricular activities including public lectures; the granting of certificates (not degrees) to both undergraduate and graduate students who undertake the American studies curriculum. The Institute has an independent budget, a director responsible only to the college, but no independent faculty. Matters of curriculum, as was the case before the establishment of the Institute, are administered by a committee composed of representatives of traditional departments.

UNDERGRADUATE PROGRAM: There is no undergraduate American studies program leading to a degree. Certificates are granted students who pursue an American studies course of study, but this must be in addition to a traditional major. A full scale undergraduate program is anticipated.

GRADUATE PROGRAM: A Ph. D. program with what amounts to a minor in American studies has been inaugurated. Theoretically, this program is open to doctoral candidates in a number of fields in the humanities; to date, however, it has only been taken advantage of by candidates for the Ph. D. in English. In this department a fixed program has been established calling for the waiver of the requirement in Anglo-Saxon, and for the completion by the student of work in American literature (at least 12 quarter hours), American history (9-12 hours), American philosophy (9-12 hours), American fine arts (9-12 hours), 9-12 hours in either anthropology, political science, or sociology, and an interdisciplinary dissertation. Students are also held responsible for the European background of one of these American fields.

GRADUATE COURSE: The graduate course is, technically, a seminar in American literature. It is designed, however, for the Ph. D. candidate in the American studies program, and devotes itself to specific topics or themes (such as travelers' observations) of an interdisciplinary character.

COMMENT: American studies activities at Utah are too patently in the developmental stage to submit to any serious evaluation. The breadth of these activities, combined with a reportedly favorable faculty attitude, furnished testimony of considerable interest. The program has already made itself felt in the addition of courses to the curriculum, as well as in other ways -- mainly extracurricular. The outsider is struck by the potential disadvantage of having one authority to administer the program (the Institute), and a separate one to administer the curriculum (the committee -- see above), although the persons involved have found no awkwardness in this arrangement. There are admitted disad-vantages, however, in the temporization resulting in the awarding of "certificates" in American studies and in the lack of an outright gradu-ate program leading to a degree in this field. In some areas, including the important one of intellectual history, course offerings are still not all they should be. Counting these debits off as growing pains, there seems to be no reason to doubt that American studies activities at Utah are well on their way to establishing an important place for themselves.

UNIVERSITY OF WICHITA, Wichita, Kansas.

Ross M. Taylor, Chairman, Department of American Civilization.

Undergraduate program leading to bachelor's degree. A two-term freshman introductory course plus a senior seminar.

1948 (lapsed 1951-54).

None.

ADMINISTRATION: American civilization, at the University of Wichita, has departmental status with control of budget, staff, and cur-riculum. Aiding the departmental chairman in the conduct of American civilization affairs is a steering committee chosen to represent the var-ious departments most active in the program. To date there has been no faculty member employed full-time in American civilization activities. The chairman of the department of American civilization is also a mem-ber of the English department; other departments active in founding and supporting the program are: history, political science, sociology, phil-osophy, and speech.

UNDERGRADUATE PROGRAM: Course and hours requirements for the B. A. in American civilization can be described roughly as follows:

> 8 hours in American civilization courses
> 15 hours in English
> 15 hours in history
> 12 hours in political science
> 6 hours in sociology
> 3 hours in philosophy.

This represents a typical emphasis, except for the rather heavy stress on political science; the department chairman has expressed a desire for more extended offerings in philosophy and in "problems" courses. Several relatively uncommon courses are listed among those recommended for American civilization majors: a history of American journalism, the American family, a course in folk literature, and a course offered by the speech department on the "Radio Industry and its Problems." The program got off to a slow start, and had only one student enrolled in 1951 when it temporarily collapsed. It was reactivated in 1954 but has attracted no majors since then.

UNDERGRADUATE COURSES: All freshmem in the American civilization program are required to take "Introduction to American Civilization," a two-term, three hour course, in which Harvey Wish's Society and Thought in America is used as a text. The first term devotes its emphasis to a comparative study of European backgrounds; the methods of the course include chronologically arranged topics, comparison of decades, the development of a culture concept, and individual research leading to term papers. Seniors are required to take "Seminar in American Civilization" which centers on the selection of a research topic by the student, class discussion and criticism, and an introduction to research methods.

COMMENT: The stated aims of this program place heavy emphasis on the study of American civilization as an emergence of European society and on the importance of America's present role in world affairs. The conduct of the program seems suited to these ends; there appears to be ample opportunity for the individual student to develop a program suited to his own needs, yet the natural emphasis of the program falls on literature (all American civilization majors take English for their minor) and on international relations (in both history and political science courses). This program is still looking for a foothold in the curriculum; to date it appears to have been sustained, in the absence of enrollment, by the popularity of the introductory course and by a cooperative attitude on behalf of both faculty and administration.

UNIVERSITY OF WISCONSIN, Madison, Wisconsin.

Undergraduate: M. L. Borrowman (education); graduate: Merle Curti (history) and Henry A. Pochman (English).

A major in American Institutions, offered in the Division of Social Studies, leading to the B. A.; two programs leading to the Ph. D., one in American Civilization (history department) and one in American Culture (English department). The undergraduate program includes a special seminar in American institutions.

Not reported.

50 undergraduate majors in American Institutions; 3 Ph. D. candidates in American Civilization; no Ph. D. Candidates in American Culture.

ADMINISTRATION: The undergraduate program is administered by a divisional committee consisting of representatives of political science, economics, history, philosophy, sociology, and geography. The doctoral program in American civilization is administered by the history department; the doctoral program in American culture, by the English department.

UNDERGRADUATE PROGRAM: This special major in the Division of Social Studies is designed for College of Letters and Science students "desiring a broad liberal knowledge of American life in a number of its phases and not specialization in a department," for School of Education students, and for students planning to enter the Law School. Of the forty credits required for the major, nineteen are specified in these fields: history, political science, economics, geography, and sociology. Also required is a three-credit seminar devoted to evaluation of American institutions, normally taken in the second semester of the senior year.

Optional courses totaling eighteen hours may be selected from art history and criticism, contemporary trends, economics, English, geography, history, history of science, journalism, philosophy, political science, psychology, social work, sociology and anthropology, and speech. Two-thirds of the optional course hours must be relevant to a theme, such as: rural life in America, urbanization and industrialization, conservation and planning in the use of American resources, implications of technology for American life, social and intellectual development, interpretations of American social development "which have originated in the University of Wisconsin," security and opportunity in American life, America and world problems, and Old World contributions to American life. Optional courses may also be chosen for their relevance to a particular area of the United States or to a historical period of the country's development.

UNDERGRADUATE COURSE: The seminar in American Institutions, noted above, is designed to integrate the students' previous study in the program. The seminar is conducted by Professor Borrowman, who often brings in guests to lecture on, and lead discussion of major social institutions. A student is required to read intensively in contemporary literature concerning American social problems and to conduct individual research consistent with the "theme of interest" in terms of which he organized his work in the program. The size of the seminar groups has been limited to eight to fifteen students.

GRADUATE PROGRAMS: The doctoral program in American civilization (history department) emphasizes social, intellectual, and economic aspects of American history. It is exceedingly flexible, varying with the candidate's preparation, background, and interest. Requirements may be grouped as follows: American history (three fields), two related fields, and a minor in a related department. The three fields of American history are selected from among "American History to 1815"; "American Nation, 1815 to 1877"; "Recent U. S. History since 1877"; "American Cultural History"; "American Economic History"; "American Foreign Relations." The two related fields are chosen to give the student's thesis research depth and breadth of setting, inasmuch as the dissertation invariably involves more than the field of history. Most often one of the related fields is "Social and Intellectual Development of Modern Europe," although the student may be excused from presenting any field of European history if his undergraduate program has included a considerable amount of it. Other related fields may be chosen from among American literature, American philosophy, American art and architecture, American political theory, American law, American social institutions, and American minority problems. A candidate must also take a minor in a department related to the fields offered in his major concentration. Usually the choice is English, philosophy, political science, art, economics, or sociology.

The doctoral program in American culture (English department) has on paper a carefully defined program designed to impart a thorough knowledge of American literature and of its backgrounds both European and American. This program remains, however, a paper program since no student has ever completed it.

COMMENT: The diversity and administrative decentralization of American studies activities at Wisconsin have prevented the accumulation of complete and detailed data covering its several phases. From correspondence, however, it would appear that active interest is confined to the undergraduate phase where the American Institutions program gives evidence, within the limits of its social science emphasis, of accomplishing its objectives with considerable success. On the graduate level, Professor Curti, although recognizing the merits of inter-disciplinary study and research, refuses to encourage enrollment in the American civilization program unless the student has a strong under-graduate background in European history. As for the American culture program, Professor Pochman estimates that interest has flagged be-cause of the sufficient breadth of the traditional departmental program in literature. To the outside observer, however, the question is whether graduate work in American studies might not be vitalized by the forma-tion of a truly interdepartmental program sponsored by both history and literature departments, and perhaps by some others as well.

UNIVERSITY OF WISCONSIN, Milwaukee 11, Wisconsin.

Marian Silveus, director of the American civilization program.

An American civilization program leading to the B. A. or the B. S.

1953.

2 undergraduate majors.

ADMINISTRATION: The program is directed by a steering com-mittee, consisting of representatives from American literature, Amer-ican history, geography, economics, political science, and sociology-anthropology. A full-fledged department is considered neither valid nor expedient.

UNDERGRADUATE PROGRAM: The major in American civiliza-tion consists of 40 credits. Requirements include three to six credits of American literature, six credits of American history, and three each of political science, geography, sociology and economics; and fourteen to nineteen optional credits elected from specified courses in English, history, geography, journalism, philosophy, political science, psychol-ogy, economics, and sociology. At least 12 credits of the optional courses must be approved by the advisor as relevant to one of the eight themes of interest listed in the catalogue.

COMMENT: In the words of the catalogue: "The work of the major provides an introduction to ideas and principles that are essential for intelligent citizenship and community leadership; and it furnishes ma-terial which is vocationally useful in such fields as journalism, law, theology, social work, government service, library work, radio and

TV, business, and teaching. Although it is primarily intended for students whose major interest is essentially interdepartmental in scope, a student may possibly combine this major with a conventional academic major." The program would be better balanced if courses in American art, music and philosophy, as well as an integrating seminar, were added to the offerings. With the expansion of the institution it is believed that the program will attract more students.

UNIVERSITY OF WYOMING, Laramie, Wyoming.

Robert H. Walker, Acting Director, School of American Studies.

Programs leading to the B. A. and M. A. including three special courses in American civilization. Summer Conference on American Studies for secondary school teachers.

1954 (although undergraduate major in American civilization had been theoretically possible since 1935, and the special summer program began in 1952).

15 undergraduate majors; 11 M. A. candidates.

ADMINISTRATION: Budgetary administration is exercised by the president of the university and the director of the School of American Studies; academic administration is exercised by a steering committee composed of official representatives of the English and history departments and the dean of the college. This arrangement is not equivalent to departmental status: in some ways there is more autonomy, and in some ways less. The budget stems from grants and bequests made by the late William Robertson Coe; funds have been used principally to increase library holdings and teaching materials, to operate the special summer conference, to underwrite scholarships and fellowships, and to allow for faculty appointments in the field.

UNDERGRADUATE PROGRAM: The objectives of the undergraduate program stress, within the framework of a broad, liberal education, the development of an appreciation of the American heritage and its present-day implications. To accomplish this general objective, two requirements have been set up. The first of these involves a core of required courses in American literature, history, and thought and including two special American civilization offerings. The second requirement forces the student to select an emphasis, either in literature, history, or the social sciences, and to take what amounts to a second major in that area. In this area of emphasis are included both American and non-American materials.

More complex and demanding than the typical liberal arts major, this program has been small, predominantly female, and of exceptionally high student calibre. Only with some recent publicity among high school seniors in the state has the enrollment grown beyond the ten scholarships offered annually. The attractiveness of the scholarships has accounted, in large measure, for student interest shown to date.

UNDERGRADUATE COURSES: "The American Experience" is required of majors during their first two years and is open to the University as an elective. Offered for the first time in 1957-58, the course attracted a fair enrollment. It was lectured by two instructors and, while centering on social and intellectual history, included materials from literature, philosophy, the fine arts, and the social sciences as well. The organization was thematic and emphasized the characterization of the civilization rather than interdisciplinary methodology.

"American Civilization" is required of majors during their last two years and is also open to graduate students. Its appeal as a general elective for undergraduates has been taken over by the lower division course and it has gone the direction of a virtual seminar for major students, utilizing a discussion method and stressing the contributions of the various disciplines to the study of the civilization.

"The American Heritage," devoted to a consideration of the European and Classical influences on the founding fathers and based on the instructor's, Wilson O. Clough's, text (Our Long Heritage), has been an upper division and graduate requirement of the program since its beginnings. The course, in fact, existed before the program and is considered as a regular offering of the English department, although it is rather a course in the history of ideas.

GRADUATE PROGRAM: The M. A. curriculum is based on a special seminar, described below, and on the development of three fields of roughly equal proportions: American history, American literature, and a third field drawn from: European history, European literature, the fine arts, or the social sciences. University requirements include 30 hours residence, a thesis, and an oral examination. At least half of the successful M. A. candidates have gone on for further graduate work in American civilization, history, literature, economics, and library science, in roughly that order. The other half have shown interest in high school teaching, journalism, and writing. Eight fellowships are awarded annually.

GRADUATE COURSE: The seminar, "Topics in American Civilization," is required of all M. A. candidates and stresses student research and the achievement of an acquaintance with the basic secondary and interpretive works in the field. "The American Heritage," described above, is also required of all graduate majors. "American Civilization" has been taken by a few graduate students and has proved helpful where the student had little interdisciplinary background.

COMMENT: The Wyoming program illustrates, both positively and negatively, the potential for American studies at the small state university. Since the humanities and social sciences have never been emphasized, there is not the wealth in course offerings or library collections on which such a program might depend. Rather, the program itself has had to attract its own core of interested students, introduce and encourage course offerings, and build library holdings; fortunately for Wyoming, the endowment has made these things possible.

As the statewide center for teacher training, on the other hand, the university has offered a ready-made area in which American studies could be applied. By virtue of a constructive relationship with both the college of education and the state department of education, the program strives in many ways to serve teachers in the state and general area, principally through its Summer Conference on American Studies (see below under "Summer 'Refresher' Programs") and through such special projects as the American Studies-Core Curriculum Workshop, held in the summers of 1957-58 and designed to produce resource units reflecting the American studies approach to the teaching of American subjects at the secondary level. Many graduates of the program enter into secondary school teaching. The distinctiveness of the Wyoming program stems from the way it has helped bring American studies into the world of the secondary school teacher without compromising in the slightest the liberal arts orientation of its courses and programs.

VASSAR COLLEGE, Poughkeepsie, New York.

Susan J. Turner (English), chairman of the committee for the American culture program.

Interdepartmental related studies major in American culture leading to the B. A. and including a special seminar.

1943.

8 candidates for the B. A.

ADMINISTRATION: As with other interdepartmental programs at Vassar, over-all supervision is provided by a coordinating Committee of the Faculty, and all of these programs are based on the assumption that students must work out a significant combination of courses from the separate, departmental disciplines. Thus American culture does not have departmental status. Founded by the departments of history, English, political science, and economics-sociology-anthropology, the American culture program operates through the joint efforts of these four central departments and the cooperating departments of philosophy, art, and geography, which offer courses in American materials. The teachers in these disciplines elect annually a chairman of the American culture program to act as executive secretary and liaison officer among the departments.

UNDERGRADUATE PROGRAM: Vassar requires all major programs to be defined in terms of "related studies." Related studies programs may be departmental or interdepartmental. The departmental programs include as many as forty points of work in a central department combined with closely correlated courses in other disciplines. These together make up the "major field," which is conceived as having greater breadth than the traditional "major-minor" requirements. Among several interdepartmental programs is one in American culture.

At the end of her sophomore year the student who elects a related studies program in American culture consults a special faculty advisor from one of the central departments to work out her program. Although the minimum course requirement for a related studies program is 45 points out of the total of 120 point required for graduation, the candidate for the American culture program usually takes considerably more than that minimum. Her program must include "range," or preparation in at least three fields related to American culture. Her program must also include "depth," or advanced work, during senior year, in at least two of the fields.

The "range" requirements include at least one year's work "of a survey nature which covers an important area of the total field" in the department of economics, English, history, or political science; she must take work in at least three of these fields.

The "depth" requirements include sequences of work leading to advanced courses in two of the central departments during the senior year, two points of "supplementary study" devoted to a senior paper written in conjunction with these advanced courses, and a senior seminar in the "Development and Culture of the United States."

UNDERGRADUATE COURSE: "Development and Culture of the United States," the special senior seminar and the only course offered directly by the program, is staffed by the members of the various departments cooperating in the program. Staff, plan, and objectives vary from year to year; but the general purpose prevails of bringing the student "to her own definition of the nature of American Culture on the basis of her particular course of study. She does this through a process of individual synthesis and group communication, adapting her pattern of synthesis to those of others in the class. She thus traces intellectually the process by which a 'culture' is created, and is tested by a discipline peculiarly relevant for Americans: that she accept both the diversity and unity of life, and then resolve them." Last year, for example, the students began with individual reports on the interrelationships of their senior courses and then made out for further discussion a list of questions arising from the reports. The rest of the term was organized around some of these questions and the topics which they gave rise to: for example, the nature of a culture, the students' home communities and what makes them American, various communities of the past (Salem, 1690; Philadelphia, 1790), the influence of the frontier, the decades of the 1920's, 1930's, 1940's. The last session was devoted to a discussion of Walter Lippman's <u>Public Philosophy.</u>

COMMENT: The program proposes "to offer the undergraduate student the opportunity to study the growth and development of American culture in three important aspects: (1) American expression in the arts; (2) American institutions -- political, economic, and social; (3) American thought." The program is a loose one both in the virtual absence of special requirements and in the flexible nature of the sole course offering. Therefore, although the goal of integration is clearly stated, a strong departmental emphasis still exists, and the success of this goal must depend to a large measure on the individual student and the guidance furnished her.

WASHINGTON AND LEE UNIVERSITY, Lexington, Virginia.

Marshall W. Fishwick, American Studies.

There is no degree program in American civilization, but special courses in American culture and civilization are offered.

1949.

ADMINISTRATION: The American civilization program at Washington and Lee was set up with the help of the history, literature, and sociology departments. Although no degree program or major concentration is offered, American studies is organized as a quasi-department with control of curriculum in the hands of a steering committee appointed by the traditional departments concerned. Unlike many schools at which the program is more extensive, it is possible for a professor at Washington and Lee to make a career in American civilization; the present professor of American studies devotes 100 per cent of his time to American studies. Full departmental status for the program is considered both valid and expedient.

UNDERGRADUATE COURSES: Three courses in American studies are offered in the college: "American Art and Architecture" examines American society as revealed through painting up to 1913 and through architecture and taste up to the present. The relationship of aesthetic expression to democracy, urbanism, industrialization, and the American way of life are explored. "Approaches to American Thought" studies the major concepts of American life and culture developed by historians, social and physical scientists, philosophers, and novelists, and applies their techniques and findings to an understanding of the American pattern. "Cultural Regions of the United States" examines the distinguishing characteristics of the regions of the United States covering such topics as the European heritage, ethnic and racial elements of the population, environmentalism, the growth of social institutions, and the philosophy of regionalism. These courses are offered under the headings of fine arts, humanities, and sociology, respectively.

COMMENT: The aims of the American civilization program are expressed in the descriptions of the three courses offered. Liberal education is the goal, and a novel approach, through the non-traditional courses cited above, the method. Faculty attitude is mixed, but the courses have proved popular with the students. Enrollment has increased every year. An interesting feature of the Washington and Lee arrangement consists of the American studies instructor offering courses under all three headings described above.

WELLS COLLEGE, Aurora, New York.

Miriam R. Small (English), Chairman, American Studies Program; W. S. Rusk (fine arts).

Major program leading to the B. A. including a special senior seminar and tutorial.

1941.

4 candidates for the B. A.

ADMINISTRATION: The American studies program at Wells is administered by an independent department. Each member of the department is also a member of a traditional department, but the American studies program has its own budgetary and curricular control, and participating faculty members do not regard their American studies participation as merely that of observers or representatives from traditional fields.

UNDERGRADUATE PROGRAM: The requirements for a student who wishes to major in American studies are (a) four courses, each a year in duration, in the fields of sociology, history of Western art, American history, and American literature; (b) four additional courses at more advanced level in fields related to American studies; and (c) a senior seminar, for the full year, in American studies. The course requirements are flexible enough to permit variation according to the interests and capacities of the students. Several of the advanced courses ("b" above) may be in one field, or they may cover a fairly wide range of fields, depending upon the program worked out by the student through consultation with her faculty advisors. One of the advanced courses may be a tutorial (not to be confused with the senior seminar) in which the student does further work under tutorial guidance: an example from recent years is a student who took tutorial work in economics designed to tie in with her preparation of a thesis on certain novels of Dreiser, and one who did work in music in connection with a thesis on coalminers' songs.

UNDERGRADUATE COURSES: The senior seminar, required of American studies majors, is built around the preparation of a thesis. The work is carried on and presented by the students, with faculty members present as critics and guides. In the first semester, there is discussion of materials being studied, presentation by students of tentative thesis outlines, suggestions for further development or needed emphases, and exchange of points of view arising from the disciplines represented. In the second semester, the students work independently, seeking advice as needed. At a series of general meetings the students read chapters from thesis drafts; criticism and suggestions follow. Faculty members from the sociology, fine arts, history, and English fields participate in the senior seminar; others join from time to time.

An optional upper division course is the American studies tutorial which is elected by the student who needs special preparation for her thesis subject: an example is given of a student who took a tutorial in economics as preparation for a thesis on Theodore Dreiser.

COMMENT: To an unusual degree, the Wells program encourages independent study by the women who elect it. There are course requirements, but the American studies program is not a mere collection of courses. The small college situation permits frequent individual consultation. Faculty participation in the individual advisory capacity as well as in the senior seminar is designed to raise questions and make suggestions from a number of different points of view. The student receives thoughtful continuing help in effecting her own integration of the various fields of study entered in her American studies work. Attention should also be called to the enthusiasm with which the interdepartmental seminar has been received by the faculty involved and to the unusual (and apparently most effective) administrative character of the offering.

WESLEYAN COLLEGE, Macon, Georgia.

Thomas F. Gossett (U. S. literature).

Undergraduate major leading to the A. B. and including a special course in American civilization.

1955.

1 major; 10 students enrolled in special course.

ADMINISTRATION: Both course and program seem to have resulted largely from the efforts of one faculty member whose primary duties are in American literature. He has served as director for the program and has considered the program as quasi-departmental in status. A recent benefaction to the American studies program plus increased evidence of interdepartmental cooperation augur well for an expanding program.

UNDERGRADUATE PROGRAM: To qualify for the program, a student must complete freshman English, foreign language, two semesters of world history, two semesters of math, two semesters of science, two semesters of religion, a survey of English literature, one semester of American literature, and six hours in either government, philosophy, psychology, or sociology. Every major student must complete a course in the history of American art and architecture, at least five courses in American history, geography, and sociology, and must complete the special two-semester American studies course. There is a strong possibility that a course in American music may be added, as the college emphasizes music.

UNDERGRADUATE COURSE: An integrating course is required of American studies majors during their final two years; this course is also designed to contribute to the liberal education pattern of the college and to emphasize the advantages of interdisciplinary study. Originally sponsored by the literature department, the course has come to enjoy participation by the sociology and religion departments. A variety of materials are used to cover such topics as: "The Supreme Court in Business," "The Scopes Trial," "Social Classes in America," and "World War I in the Novels of the 20s." F. L. Allen's The Big Change serves as a unifying text. The several faculty members invite considerable discussion and student reports, and require a considerable number of papers in lieu of examination. As this course becomes known, there are increasing indications of its popularity.

COMMENT: Still in its formative stage, this program has frankly imitated the Minnesota program and has modeled its course on the Princeton idea. The religious sponsorship of Wesleyan gives some distinctive flavor to the curriculum, and the director announces that the greatest need is for a thorough course in American social and intellectual history. The newly received funds are to be used mainly for library acquisitions and for visiting lectureships -- the latter having already been used to great advantage.

WEST VIRGINIA UNIVERSITY, Morgantown, W. Virginia.

Stephen Crocker (English), Chairman of Integrated Studies.

Special course in American civilization.

1948.

ADMINISTRATION: The American civilization course is offered under the direction of the humanities program in Integrated Studies. Although the direction was originally under a steering committee, it has now passed into the hands of the chairman. It would appear the course originated through the action of the English, philosophy, art and music departments and was opposed by the history department. There is no intention at present of establishing an independent American civilization department, nor is such a plan considered either valid or expedient; rather the course is seen as part of the Integrated Studies program.

UNDERGRADUATE COURSE: The course is given on the junior-senior level and is conducted by lecture and discussion led by single individuals or by student symposia. The content and organization are currently under study and revision so that no complete description is possible at present. However, the disciplines of art, architecture, history, music, literature, philosophy, and religion are involved, and the course used original materials as well as secondary works. The course is conceived to be a liberal education course in humanities and is elective.

COMMENT: American civilization at West Virginia is clearly more a branch of general education than an autonomous program. The course is presented as one among several humanities courses, not as an integrating course surrounded by a number of related courses dealing with American materials. While this situation doubtless reflects a thriving humanities department there, it is also probable that the opposition of the history department has had something to do with this evolution. The course has proven moderately popular with steadily rising enrollment.

WESTERN MARYLAND COLLEGE, Westminster, Maryland.

Richard B. Hovey (English), in charge, American Civilization Major Program.

American Civilization Program leading to the B. A. degree and including one course in American civilization.

1945.

10 candidates for the B. A.

ADMINISTRATION: The program operates entirely within the English department and serves as one of six objectives to be elected by English majors. Administrative responsibility, then, falls to the department chairman.

UNDERGRADUATE PROGRAM: Prerequisites for the major in American civilization include, in the freshman and sophomore years, two semesters of American history, one semester of American literature, two semesters of English literature, and one semester of American government; in the junior and senior years, majors are required to take two semesters of American literature, one semester of American studies, one semester of American philosophy, one semester of American art, one semester of American social history, one semester of English language, and one semester of American and English contemporary literature. Towards improving the American civilization program, there has been added the interdisciplinary course described below.

UNDERGRADUATE COURSE: A one-semester course in "Intellectual and Social Backgrounds of American Literature," designed to become an integral and synthesizing part of the American civilization program at Western Maryland, was introduced in the fall of 1956. For a basic text Horton and Edwards, Backgrounds of American Literary Thought, was used. Secondary texts owned by students and used for collateral readings were Nevins and Commager, Pocket History of the U. S.; Flexner, Pocket History of American Painting; Heffner, Documentary History of the U. S.; Tunnard and Reed, American Skyline; Hofstadter, American Political Tradition; Burlingame, Machines that Built America; and Lewis, Babbitt. Other readings were assigned from library holdings. The course surveyed American culture from colonial times to the present, emphasizing particularly the relationships among social conditions, intellectual history, and literature, but also including sketches of the history of American art, architecture, city-planning, and political ideology. The purpose was to achieve a historical grasp of issues which are still alive today, such as the cultural interdependence of Europe and America, the Negro problem, etc. Student reaction to the course has been favorable, but both students and instructor agreed that the course was overcrowded and should be developed into a two-semester offering.

COMMENT: As an alternative degree program for English majors, this curriculum has evidently had appeal from its inception, and the addition of the integrating course has solidified its effect. Theoretical disadvantages of such a program within a single department include the difficulty of interdisciplinary work, and lack of control of courses outside the department. Yet both of these seem to have been overcome, at least to some measure. The integrating course has provided at least some interdisciplinary experience; and the history department, it is reported, has been influenced by the program to include more social and intellectual history in its courses.

WESTERN RESERVE UNIVERSITY, Cleveland, Ohio.

Lyon Richardson (English), Chairman, Graduate Committee on American Culture.

Degree-granting programs on all levels: B. A., M. A., and Ph. D. special courses in American culture included on all three levels.

1936 (undergraduate); 1938 (graduate).

8 candidates for the B. A.; 18 candidates for the M. A.; 17 candidates for the Ph. D.

ADMINISTRATION: The program is administered by a chairman and steering committee, the members of which are appointed as official representatives of traditional departments of English, history, political science, sociology, art and geography. This committee however constitutes a quasi-department with control of curriculum. The program was established by the departments of history, literature and sociology, and is still conceived as an interdepartmental major. Departmental status is considered invalid; and, although credit toward promotion is given for teaching in the program, there is no future for an instructor in American civilization unless he is hired in one of the traditional departments.

UNDERGRADUATE PROGRAM: The program is a major program leading to the B. A. The prerequisites for the major are courses in sociology, political science, and economics. Majors are required to take courses in art, history, literature, philosophy, geography, and political science, and must carry 48 credits (12 more than the ordinary major requires). Thirty-three credits out of the 48 are devoted to a prescribed curriculum including sociology, political science, history, economics, geography, English, and the American culture seminar. The remaining 15 are elective and must be advanced courses. Out of the entire 48 credits, 12 must be taken in each of two fields, which two must be chosen from among the following six: economics, geography, English, history, political science, and sociology. The students are mostly men, with few foreign students, and of average ability. There is some extracurricular activity: lectures and a student club.

UNDERGRADUATE COURSE: The American culture seminar is organized either around a single theme or selected topics and is taught by discussion with visiting lecturers. The teaching load varies; usually one person devotes 1/4 time to it while others contribute special lectures. The aim of the course is liberal education, but it is designed to present a new approach to American culture. The emphasis is contemporary and involves art, history, literature, and philosophy.

GRADUATE PROGRAM: After a slow start, the graduate program reached a level in about 1944 which it has maintained ever since. Although practically any emphasis among the humanities and social sciences is possible, about two-thirds of the graduate students concentrate on literature and the remaining one-third on history.

The M. A. program is based on 30 hours required work. The usual program requires courses in history, literature, art, philosophy, sociology. The student may either take a seminar and produce in it a monograph, or write a thesis. A four hour written examination on a selected reading list is required for the degree.

The Ph. D. program requires 78 hours beyond the B. A., no more than 12 of which may be taken on the dissertation. The usual language requirements are in force. The preliminary examination consists of two written papers on his major fields, plus an oral on five fields from four of the following departments: economics, English, education, fine arts, history, philosophy, political science, and sociology. The dissertation is supervised jointly by two men and must evidently combine at least two fields, each advisor representing a different one.

GRADUATE COURSES: Under the title of American culture, graduate courses prepare students for the M. A. thesis and the Ph. D. dissertation. Aside from this consistent purpose, the seminars have varied widely in content from year to year, offering such subjects as: the philosophy of modern poetry, the concept of democracy in American literature, the frontier hypothesis, and so forth. The course is staffed by various members of the interested faculty, and use is often made of special lectures in addition.

COMMENT: The entire program has been very favorably received on the Western Reserve campus at all levels. Featuring a program well balanced between the social sciences and the humanities, the undergraduate curriculum has been found useful especially for prospective high school teachers, law students, and businessmen. The avowed aim of the program is the study and interpretation of American culture, both in respect to its relations to other cultures and to its unique characteristics.

The M. A. program has been found suitable for teachers, especially, and for such non-teaching fields as the ministry, public relations, journalism, and editing. At neither the M. A. nor the Ph. D. level has there reportedly been any difficulty in placing degree-holders, although in college teaching most opportunities are found in traditional departments. The graduate program has been called upon to absorb students with widely varied backgrounds and interests; it has done this with apparent success, although maintaining a strong literary emphasis.

WHEATON COLLEGE, Wheaton, Illinois. *

S. R. Kamm, Chairman, Division of Social Sciences.

An undergraduate program leading to the bachelor degree in social science with an emphasis on American studies.

1946.

One undergraduate major.

ADMINISTRATION: Formerly a full-fledged major program, the American studies curriculum has recently been subordinated, administratively, to the social science division. The major program is still in effect; but it is no longer, technically, a degree-granting program. It is administered by the chairman and staff of the social science division who feel no need to move toward separate status for American studies.

UNDERGRADUATE PROGRAM: The program exists in recognition of the advantages of a broad training in American culture both for general education and for such specific careers as the ministry, law, teaching, and publishing. An interdepartmental major, the program requires courses at the lower division level in American history and literature and in the history of Western civilization. Elective course work usually falls into such additional areas as art, music, philosophy, religion, and the social sciences.

A senior seminar in American civilization has been discontinued and has been replaced, as a requirement, by the proseminar in social science. As did its predecessor, this course seeks to integrate the various materials encountered by the student in his interdepartmental major. Obviously, the limitations imposed by this proseminar prevent the treatment of some of the American studies disciplines necessarily encountered in the curriculum.

COMMENT: Enrollment in the American studies program has always been slight and irregular at Wheaton, averaging only three or four students. Interests formerly active in the program -- notably literature -- have withdrawn so that students now concentrate exclusively in such areas as history, political science, or sociology. Although students still take course work in literature, philosophy, and the fine arts, the emphasis has definitely shifted to the social sciences.

WHITTIER COLLEGE, Whittier, California.

James M. Merrill, (history), Acting Chairman, History Department.

Undergraduate American civilization course.

1935.

ADMINISTRATION: The required sophomore course in American civilization is taught collaboratively by two faculty members whose professional background is in history and literature, respectively, and who administer the course on a quasi-departmental basis. Their basic administrative identification is with the traditional departments to which they belong; their work with the American civilization course, however, offers opportunities for professional advancement which equal those in a departmental situation.

UNDERGRADUATE COURSE: The course in American civilization is strongly oriented toward literature and history, but it also embraces artistic, philosophic, economic, and religious aspects of the American experience. Chronologically, the course covers the period from colonial times to 1900, giving attention to life in the North, the South, and the West. Emphasis is placed upon such important trends as transcendentalism, sectionalism, realism. Throughout the course, the growth of democratic, Christian institutions is stressed. Lectures are presented three times a week to the entire class; in a fourth meeting, the class meets in small discussion sections led by student assistants. Vernon L. Parrington's Main Currents in American Thought is used as a text, without further textual or source reading.

COMMENT: The fact that the American civilization course is required, and that Parrington's work is used as a text indicates that the course aims mainly to provide the general student with a citizen's appreciation of the social aspects of American institutions, ideals, and literature. On this basis, the course has been successful and well-received during its relatively long career at the College. The historical approach, combined with a regard for sectional problems and characteristics, is consistent with such aims. It may, however, limit the possibility of studying aesthetic, philosophic, and religious phenomena except as manifestations of social, and probably principally political, movements.

WILLIAMS COLLEGE, Williamstown, Massachusetts.

Luther S. Mansfield and Charles R. Keller, co-directors of major. (C. Fredrick Rudolph, acting for Professor Keller, 1955-56; 1956-57.)

Major in American history and literature leading to A. B. degree and including a special course.

1940 -- to take effect for class of 1942.

26 in class of 1957; 18 in class of 1956.

ADMINISTRATION: This major is under the supervision of two directors who constitute a kind of steering committee with control of the curriculum. The budget and staff are part of the history department, as indeed are the two directors, one of whom is now chairman of the department. The other director, trained in American literature, was transferred to the history department.

UNDERGRADUATE PROGRAM: As indicated, this program is entitled a major in American history and literature, but courses in art, philosophy, government and economics are among those that may be chosen by students to fulfill major requirements. The introductory courses in European history and literature are, of course, required of all majors, as are introductory courses in other fields in which the student may want to take advanced work as part of his major. In the junior or senior years, majors must take American literature and American social and intellectual history. In their senior year, majors must take American history and literature, a course designed for and limited to these majors. Honors majors devote the equivalent of two full-year courses to the preparation of an honors thesis. This major in American history and literature is a popular one at Williams and ranks among the first five in number of students enrolled (second in 1956-57).

UNDERGRADUATE COURSE: A double course in American history and literature is designed for and required of all majors. This course is taught by the two co-directors of the major who describe it as "a critical study of American ideas and values." The content of the course varies from year to year, but usually includes, at one pole, a study of Puritanism and, at the other, a critical reading of some book published within the preceding year. The course attempts by reading and discussing some of the "great books" in the field to explore some of the assumptions of the disciplines of history and literature and to correlate many aspects of American civilization.

COMMENT: The primary aim of this major is to acquaint intelligent American college students with the American past and present so that, among other things, they may learn more about themselves. As in other programs of a similar character, much of its success depends presumably upon the impact upon the student of the special course designed for the major. It is significant that at Williams this important course is the equivalent of two full-year courses in other fields.

WILSON COLLEGE, Chambersburg, Pennsylvania.

Dora Mae Clark (history and political science), Advisor in American civilization.

Major program leading to B. A. and including one special course.

1948.

4 undergraduate majors.

ADMINISTRATION: The program is administered by the chairman of the political science department, who is also professor of American history. There is no steering committee. The program was established by a subcommittee of the curriculum committee of the college, the initiative being taken by members of the history department. Although credit for promotion is given for teaching in this program on an equal basis with teaching in any other, there is no future for someone wishing to teach nothing but American civilization and no prospect of departmental status.

UNDERGRADUATE PROGRAM: The program is a major program including an American civilization course. The program is interdepartmental, with major emphasis on history and literature. Six semester courses are required in history and three in other fields including literature, sociology, political science, Bible, art, and economics. (The program has consistently been among the largest ten in the school.)

UNDERGRADUATE COURSE: The American civilization course is a seminar course which attempts to give intensive study in several areas and to correlate these areas with each other. It is usually organized either around selected topics or the culture concept and is conducted through discussion led by specialists. The first semester is devoted to training in the concept and methods of culture analysis under the direction of a single faculty member. The second is devoted to specific topics, including art, architecture, history, literature, philosophy, religion, economics, and sociology. The course focuses on the present against the background of the past and provides generous bibliography in all fields covered.

COMMENT: The program at Wilson is typical of the small college situation particularly in two ways. First, there is no feeling for further administrative elaboration of the program: those concerned are content to leave the interdepartmental program a non-departmental one. Secondly, the advisor for the program frankly states that the student is expected to take the initiative in "correlating" or "integrating" the various materials that make up her approach to the study of a civilization. In a larger institution, this admission would be one of failure in most cases; in a small college such as this one, the close personal supervision available makes good results under such conditions possible. The purpose of this program, then, could be fairly stated as an effort to provide liberal education in a number of fields, the American content being relevant chiefly as a point where these fields may be brought together.

WITTENBERG COLLEGE, Springfield, Ohio.

William Coyle (English).

Undergraduate major in American civilization including two special courses.

1950.

The major is so recent that enrollment figures are not available; the courses typically fill their limited enrollment of thirty.

ADMINISTRATION: The American civilization program represents an interdepartmental major administered by the two departments of history and literature. These two were responsible for establishing the program and have evidently kept it going ever since, despite mixed reactions from other faculty members. Owing to the size of the college, it is not felt that an independent department of American civilization is either valid or expedient, and accordingly there is no career to be made in that field alone. Students may major either in history or literature or in the interdepartmental major itself.

UNDERGRADUATE PROGRAM: This newly established major stresses courses in American history and literature and includes further interdepartmental work in such fields as art, philosophy, political science, and sociology. The requirement of 45 hours course work within the major is no higher than other interdepartmental majors at Wittenberg, but considerably higher than traditional majors.

UNDERGRADUATE COURSES: Included in the major requirement are two special courses in American civilization conducted on the discussion principle and staffed by one member of the history and one of the literature department, both of whom are present at all sessions. The course which originated the Wittenberg program involves a three-year chronological cycle covering (1) the Revolution, (2) the Civil War, and (3) the Frontier. This course is taken in the junior and/or senior year and, presumably, no more than two years of the cycle is expected.

Recently another special course has been offered dealing with such themes as pragmatism, Puritanism, and so forth, and aiming at a more general level suitable to lower class election.

COMMENT: The program is designed to promote the integration of materials presented by separate departments and to produce a new outlook on American life. The methodology of such a process is ignored and actual materials are the focus of efforts in the special courses. The recent addition of a new course and of the undergraduate major testify to the strong and serious interest in this activity on the part of both faculty and students.

YALE UNIVERSITY, New Haven, Connecticut.

David M. Potter, Chairman, American Studies Program.

Program leading to B. A. and Ph. D. degrees. Undergraduate program includes two courses in American studies for majors, three for honors candidates.

1945. American civilization course first offered in 1931.

A. B. candidates: 230; Ph. D. candidates: 16.

ADMINISTRATION: The American studies program at Yale is under the direction of a chairman and a steering committee with control of budget and curriculum, but not of staff. Appointments are made jointly with a traditional department. The program, interestingly, represents the outgrowth of the department of "History, the Arts and Letters" which itself provided for degree-granting programs in the American area. Even this broad area, it was felt, was insufficient for a complete exploration of the subject; hence, the current program was established to admit such disciplines as economics and the social sciences. Gifts to Yale from William R. Coe (an important collection of Western Americana and a sizeable bequest) have drawn additional attention to American studies. Since Yale counts such bequests as part of the general University endowment, administrative effects of this gift have been indirect.

UNDERGRADUATE PROGRAM: The undergraduate program in American studies is essentially an interdepartmental major involving courses in history, literature, social sciences, philosophy and art. Requirements include a full-year course in introductory American history in the sophomore year, and three courses in the junior and senior years, namely: "American Thought and Civilization," "American Literature," and a coordinating seminar. The program also includes choices of several courses such as "History of Philosophy," "History of Art," and "Intellectual History of Europe." Candidates for honors in American studies, under a new program begun in 1956, do not take courses from the regular curriculum, but enroll in two intensive seminars for junior year and two for senior year. This major is the second most popular in the college, and there has been an increase in its popularity as it has become better known.

UNDERGRADUATE COURSES: All majors must take a full year course in "American Thought and Civilization," a large lecture course, not limited to American studies majors, which is essentially a survey of the main currents of American intellectual history. In addition, standard majors take a coordinating seminar in their senior year. The topics upon which this seminar is based vary from year to year but are all chosen for their integrative value. The seminar for honors majors in junior year deals with American institutions and American thought; for senior year with American literature and with concepts of the American character. In their senior year, honors majors also take a seminar in which they work on individual research topics. American studies tutorials are also required of honors students during their last two years.

GRADUATE PROGRAM: Every candidate for the Ph. D. must prepare himself for examination in American history and American literature and two other related fields. Each student is urged to take enough work in the traditional areas of history or literature to qualify for a teaching appointment in one of these departments. There are no graduate courses which are offered as distinctively American studies courses. Yale does, however, offer a summer refresher course in American studies for high school teachers following the general pattern of other universities with W. R. Coe subsidies.

COMMENT: The principal aim of both the undergraduate and graduate programs at Yale is to provide a course of study that cuts across departmental lines and, therefore, provides a broader point of view and wider perspective than the traditional programs. One of the aims of the undergraduate program is to provide the student with concepts and materials that will help him to integrate various aspects of American civilization. This is particularly true of the honors program which includes seminars based on cultural and institutional concepts and their application to the contemporary American scene. The graduate program, at least as reflected in course offerings, does not appear to have this analytical focus.

DIRECTORY SUPPLEMENT

The entries described above can better be understood in terms of what the survey did not attempt to, or was not able to cover. Some of the activities in American studies at the college level did not conform closely enough to the general pattern so that they might be justifiably included in a parallel listing with those mentioned above. Correspondence with some institutions produced negative or uncertain results. Some phases of American studies activity seemed to need special treatment. This supplementary section will serve to clarify the focus of the survey and to provide special treatment for those exceptional cases.

VARIATIONS ON AMERICAN STUDIES

One purpose of this survey has been to describe interdisciplinary offerings in the American area. Often such work is carried on so unselfconsciously, or in a manner so consistently subservient to some separate purpose, that those responsible for it have not seen fit to label their work as belonging within a discussion of American studies activity. On such situations we do not pretend to have anything approaching a full report; yet these variations on the theme of American studies are often most interesting.

American studies courses, for example, are utilized for widely different purposes. At the NEW SCHOOL FOR SOCIAL RESEARCH, American studies courses are used merely to broaden the historical approach within a standard curriculum; at PACE COLLEGE, where business preparation is the main emphasis, such courses are used to provide a basic survey of American institutions. As an example of a course with an opposite function, there is the experimental course in what might be called American studies used to explain the American businessman (as analyzed by the historian, political scientist, economist, sociologist, philosopher, psychologist, and modern entrepreneur) to the essentially liberal arts students at the UNIVERSITY OF CALIFORNIA, RIVERSIDE CAMPUS. At FISK UNIVERSITY a lower division course in American civilization is used to enrich the offerings provided advanced students who enter under the "early admissions plan"; while at the Upper Montclair NEW JERSEY STATE TEACHERS COLLEGE courses in American studies, underwritten by the Sloan Foundation, are being used as "field studies in American life" to aid in the education of future teachers.

Sometimes the "sponsorship" of programs in American studies becomes so complete that an independent program can hardly be said to exist; rather, the special curriculum serves more truly as an alternative to, or as an elaboration of, the offering of a department, division, or other special program. The most common of such sponsoring agents appears to be the history department: at FRANKLIN AND MARSHALL COLLEGE this department allows its majors to form a program from such courses outside its own offerings as literature, government, and philosophy; at ST. FRANCIS COLLEGE the history department offers a similar curriculum with the idea of providing a broader emphasis to its own departmental majors; at the UNIVERSITY OF SCRANTON history majors are invited to relate their work in the American area with their minor programs in other disciplines so as to achieve an American civilization emphasis. In similar manner, English departments offer controlled curricula; at the UNIVERSITY OF CHATTANOOGA, for example, the student majoring in literature may depart from the traditional program at the end of two years and elect courses in art, history, and philosophy so as to round out his interdepartmental experience in subjects American. At CALIFORNIA STATE POLYTECHNIC COLLEGE it is the department of social sciences which sponsors a major program involving work in more than one discipline; while at MICHIGAN STATE UNIVERSITY it is the division of social science which offers, as one of its "distributed major" programs, a curriculum in American studies.

As an example of sponsorship by special program, there is the offering of the UNIVERSITY OF CHICAGO in this field which exists within the framework of a series of "History of Culture" alternatives. Based on a core of course work in general cultural history, curricula may then be chosen with geographic limits (French studies, Latin studies, American studies) and with contributions from courses in literature, philosophy, the fine arts, and other subjects in addition to history. These programs extend not only to the A. B. degree, but to the M. A. and Ph. D. as well. The broadest sponsorship of all -- that of the college itself--is exemplified by the SCRIPPS COLLEGE curriculum which, by requiring an individualistic, thematic upper-level "concentration" of course work often leads students to elect such a pattern of courses that interdisciplinary experience in the American area results.

In addition to its uses in the normal undergraduate course and curriculum structure, American studies activities have also found special "extra-curricular" places for themselves. Since often such situations cannot lend themselves to the most serious interdisciplinary efforts, and since they are outside the main academic stream, they are not well suited for a survey of this type. For examples of this type of activity one can refer to the summer program for French teachers at the University of Washington (described under summer "refresher" programs) or to the program for foreign students at GOSHEN COLLEGE. Open to any foreign student with a high school diploma or its equivalent, the curriculum covers two years of course work in religion, psychology, sociology, economics, and American literature, history and government. No integrative work is attempted; offerings are simply chosen from existing courses in the departments indicated, except for an introductory "speech and orientation" class. At the end of the two years, a "certificate of American Studies" is awarded.

SUMMER "REFRESHER" PROGRAMS IN AMERICAN STUDIES

Several of the institutions described in foregoing sections offer extensions of their regular American studies activities during summer sessions; others have special summer activities which have already been described. The tendency in these special summer programs, some of which have not elsewhere been mentioned in this report, has been to focus on the intellectual needs of public school teachers in the humanities and social science areas. Various approaches have been taken to the subject matter offered -- some regional, some stressing one discipline more than others, some thematic. Continuously evident, however, has been the assumption that the American studies summer program was to provide the active teacher (usually the secondary school teacher) with a fresh and stimulating review of selected aspects of American civilization, and that the target in these sessions was to be the teacher's own mind rather than a stock of classroom materials.

The main force in the encouragement of such activity has been the American Studies Program (directed by Mr. Samuel Pettingill) of the Coe Foundation of New York City. By working first with those institutions endowed directly by the late William Robertson Coe, the Foundation has endeavored to establish a pattern for summer refresher courses which could be followed on a nationwide scale. The first of these endowed programs was offered, in 1952, by the UNIVERSITY OF WYOMING when some twenty teachers of literature and social studies in the high schools of that state were invited to participate (with the aid of fellowships) in a five-week session devoted to the study of American thought, literature, and history. Since that summer, teachers have been invited at the rate of 50 a summer (two groups of twenty-five each for each five-week term) to take three courses (one in American literature and philosophy, one in American social and intellectual history, and one conference course tailored to individual interests) for five graduate credits. Distinguished lecturers from other universities in these fields have been brought each term for one of these courses plus a series of public lectures. Geographically the program has expanded and now invites teachers from several states, principally in the Midwest and Rocky Mountain areas.

The Wyoming program has been described with some detail since, according to the will of the benefactor, it must serve as a model for other such programs subject to his benefaction. Of the originally endowed institutions, YALE UNIVERSITY has adhered most closely to this form (in fact it was a Yale professor who helped inaugurate the Wyoming program), limiting itself, as far as participants go, to Connecticut teachers. STANFORD UNIVERSITY, presenting its program through its Institute of American History, has confined its offerings more to the presentation of themes and interpretations within American history. Teachers have been drawn mainly from California, but a wider representation has sometimes occurred and is anticipated for the future.

In the summer of 1957, the Coe Foundation endowed seven more institutions with a total of $58,000 for the purpose of initiating summer programs similar to those described above. These institutions were: ABILENE CHRISTIAN COLLEGE, DEPAUW UNIVERSITY, LORETTO HEIGHTS COLLEGE, RIPON COLLEGE, TRINITY COLLEGE (Washington, D.C.), TULANE UNIVERSITY, and the COLLEGE OF WOOSTER. For the summer of 1958 five more institutions were added while only one (College of Wooster) of those already in operation has been discontinued; this brings to fifteen the total number of summer programs sponsored by the Coe Foundation. The latest additions are: TUSKEGEE INSTITUTE, UNIVERSITY OF CHATTANOOGA, UNIVERSITY OF MIAMI (Florida), UNIVERSITY OF SOUTH CAROLINA, and WEST VIRGINIA WESLYAN UNIVERSITY. Further subsidies are anticipated, both to increase geographical coverage and to add to the variety in types and religions represented by these institutions. Considering the endowment in the nature of an incentive, the Foundation hopes that the institutions themselves, or other benefactors, will be able to take over the operation of the refresher programs, once established.

Two further institutions offering similar programs have come to our attention: LOS ANGELES STATE COLLEGE inaugurated in the summer of 1956 an Institute of American Studies for primary and secondary school teachers. Designed especially for teachers whose classrooms contained students of Mexican ancestry mixed with students of other national backgrounds, the Institute stressed courses dealing with acculturation, with Mexican history and art, with American-Mexican relations in the Southwest, and with special educational problems in the region. For further data on this program, see American Studies II (March, 1957) 1-2. (Committee meetings have also been in session on this campus with the object of setting up B. A. and M. A. courses of study in American studies.) Another institution which reports itself in the "planning stages" of full year American studies development has also offered a "Summer Workshop in American Studies" for the first time in 1957. This UNIVERSITY OF MASSACHUSETTS program was advertised as "of special interest to high school teachers in the fields of English, history, and the social sciences who are taking work for professional improvement," and offered courses in American linguistics, intellectual history and literature.

The idea of summer work in American studies has stretched so far as to accommodate visitors to our shores, as evidenced by the "American Civilization Institute for Teachers from France" held at the UNIVERSITY OF WASHINGTON during the summer of 1957. This unusual program, "designed to present...a balanced, orderly, and representative experience of American scholarship and American life," was based on a series of lectures dealing mainly with American fine arts, literature, and lingual usages. Not content to rely on the classroom situation alone, those in charge of this session organized tours and visits so as to point out, at first hand, such aspects of American life as: public works, private industry, natural resources, family and home life, recreation and entertainment, graphic arts, education, and scenery.

The mutual attraction between American studies curricula and secondary school teachers can be explained in several ways: the fact that teachers are often called upon to teach in more than one area, the well of student interest in the native land which can be drawn on with pedagogical effect, to suggest two. A more recent source of attraction stems from the development of core curricula on the junior- and senior-high levels. Here teachers are asked not only to handle more than one subject in a single class, but also actively to provide for the meaningful assimilation of diverse materials. This task is, of course, exactly what is involved in most American studies situations at whatever level. As an example of this new common interest, the Wyoming State Department of Education and the Wyoming University College of Education (with the endorsement of the American studies program) successfully petitioned for a separate subsidy from the Coe Foundation in order to undertake a two-summer workshop devoted to the development of resource units for junior high and eleventh grade core curricula based on an American studies approach. The first session of the workshop was held in 1957.

NEW PROGRAMS IN AMERICAN STUDIES

During the course of the survey, a few institutions indicated their intentions to inaugurate programs in American studies or reported on programs recently put into operation. Because, in all cases, the data on such programs -- their reception by faculty, administration, and student body, their effects on student careers and curricula -- were necessarily incomplete, it was felt that they had best be acknowledged in a group and by a few words each. The information relevant to these offerings could not be made to stand the detailed analysis given to the programs and courses of longer standing.

In connection with its School of International Service, THE AMERICAN UNIVERSITY has formulated careful plans for a program in American culture centering around the initiation of a 12-hour course to include such aspects of our culture as: demography, government, aesthetic expression, business, and philosophy. This potential program has been developed by a committee headed by Roy Basler of the Library of Congress and including several other distinguished representatives of local institutions. The program, scheduled to begin in September of 1958, is to operate on both undergraduate and graduate levels and aims to present a comparative approach to the understanding of social systems as integrated entities. Also in the planning stage is a program at BOSTON UNIVERSITY which has been the subject of a series of conferences held by representatives of the history and literature departments. Already being offered are one undergraduate course called "The History of American Civilization" (social and intellectual history) and an M. A. program combining American history and literature. With such beginnings, it has been hoped that a truly interdepartmental program in the American area could be established.

Officially announced during the spring of 1957, a new program in American studies is now being offered by BOWLING GREEN STATE UNIVERSITY. The departments of art, history, literature, philosophy, and political science were responsible for the initiation of this under-graduate major, and they administer it through a steering committee. The curriculum consists of six hours of work recommended by each of the departments involved and is climaxed by a senior seminar wherein these diverse materials will be brought together in relation to a theme selected from the nation's cultural past. Another undergraduate pro-gram being offered for the first time in 1957 is at STATE UNIVERSITY TEACHERS COLLEGE at New Paltz, New York. Sponsored by the Division of Social Science, the American studies program is one of several options within the division which stress either regional or dis-ciplinary approaches. The core of this program rests in a lower-level course in American institutions which uses a social science organization to describe social, political, and economic aspects of our civilization. Further requirements include literature, history, and political science; electives may be chosen from such topics as geography, current history, foreign relations, and Canadian history.

Whereas the UNIVERSITY OF TEXAS has offered a graduate pro-gram in American civilization since 1944 (on which we have been unable to obtain information), this institution has announced an undergraduate program for the first time in 1957. Impetus has been provided by the departments of anthropology, art, history, literature, philosophy, and sociology; the curriculum consists simply of a major in one of the above departments with an emphasis on the American area. No special course has been proposed. UTAH STATE AGRICULTURAL COLLEGE is also offering for the first time in 1957 an undergraduate major in American studies without special course. Sponsorship here rests with the English department in cooperation with the School of Social Sciences; curricular requirements consist of selected existing courses in literature (Ameri-can and European), history, and political science. To complete the major, the student must elect his remaining courses from at least two of the following areas: art, economics, education, music, or sociology.

INACTIVE PROGRAMS

In describing activity at the various institutions, some effort has been made to indicate the extent of quantitative participation. Some of the programs described had been virtually inactive for certain periods. Other institutions, many of which have no doubt escaped our attention, have enjoyed little or no participation throughout the history of their offerings. One such is the "American Culture: Contemporary" under-graduate major at THE CITY COLLEGE OF NEW YORK where a recent survey of graduates showed that only one out of 2,000 had elected this program. The reason offered for this lack of interest emphasizes the absence of career possibilities stemming from such a course of study. For certain career-training programs (such as pre-law, teacher training in secondary school social studies, and sociology) students are often advised to adopt an overlapping curriculum which includes much of the American culture major. Students pursuing these overlapping programs have been numerous in recent years (e.g., in 1954, 73 in pre-law; 59 in sociology; 37 in social studies teacher training), which fact may help explain the inactivity of the American culture major.

DEPAUW UNIVERSITY announces that it has "recently" inaugurated an American area major program on the undergraduate level, but has so far had no takers. A summer program in American studies for high school teachers was offered in 1957, however (see above). In 1952 the UNIVERSITY OF OKLAHOMA drew up a 36-hour undergraduate major in American studies based on existing courses in history, literature, and government; here also (as of January, 1957) there have been no students enrolled. Within its Intercultural Studies curricula WESTERN COLLEGE FOR WOMEN has for some time offered a concentration in United States Civilization. Required courses are drawn from existing offerings in art, history, economics, literature, political science, religion, and sociology, plus a special course titled "Intercultural Studies." Aspects of this program dealing with foreign civilizations have attracted active participation; no student has as yet elected to follow the United States Civilization curriculum.

The following list represents institutions where, through direct correspondence, it was determined that no American studies activity existed. They fall into three classes: institutions which have had American studies courses and/or programs in the past but have abandoned them; institutions which anticipate activity in the as yet indefinite future; institutions which, at some stage of the survey, indicated the presence of American studies activity but which decided, on further consideration, that their offerings were not really in this field. These institutions are:

ALMA COLLEGE
CHATHAM COLLEGE
COLLEGE OF PUGET SOUND
DUKE UNIVERSITY
EASTERN WASHINGTON COLLEGE OF EDUCATION
HAMPTON INSTITUTE
INCARNATE WORD COLLEGE
INDIANA UNIVERSITY
JOHNS HOPKINS UNIVERSITY
MANHATTANVILLE COLLEGE OF THE SACRED HEART
MARYMOUNT COLLEGE (New York)

- 151 -

MERCYHURST COLLEGE
MEREDITH COLLEGE
MIDDLEBURY COLLEGE
MURRAY STATE COLLEGE
NORTHWESTERN UNIVERSITY
OHIO STATE UNIVERSITY
OUACHITA BAPTIST COLLEGE
PENNSYLVANIA STATE UNIVERSITY
ST. BONAVENTURE UNIVERSITY
SOUTHERN ILLINOIS UNIVERSITY
STATE COLLEGE OF WASHINGTON
STATE TEACHERS COLLEGE (Florence, Alabama)
TARKIO COLLEGE
TEACHERS COLLEGE AT OSWEGO (New York)
TEXAS TECHNOLOGICAL COLLEGE
TRINITY UNIVERSITY (Texas)
UNIVERSITY OF CALIFORNIA AT LOS ANGELES
UNIVERSITY OF CINCINNATI
UNIVERSITY OF COLORADO
UNIVERSITY OF KENTUCKY
UNIVERSITY OF LOUISVILLE
UNIVERSITY OF TAMPA
WESTERN ILLINOIS STATE COLLEGE

INSTITUTIONS NOT RESPONDING TO THE SURVEY

Most of the following institutions responded to inquiries in the initial stages of the survey by returning post cards, indicating the existence of an American studies program, course, or both. With the others, the preliminary correspondence did not lead to conclusive results. The Committee regrets that it is, therefore, unable to report on the state of American studies at these colleges.

EASTERN OREGON COLLEGE OF EDUCATION
EAST TEXAS STATE TEACHERS COLLEGE
GEORGE WILLIAMS COLLEGE
LAKE FOREST COLLEGE
MEMPHIS STATE COLLEGE
NORTHWEST MISSOURI STATE COLLEGE
OKLAHOMA STATE UNIVERSITY
ROCKHURST COLLEGE
ST. AUGUSTINE'S COLLEGE

SOUTHERN OREGON COLLEGE OF EDUCATION
SOUTHWESTERN UNIVERSITY
TEXAS CHRISTIAN UNIVERSITY
UNIVERSITY OF DELAWARE (see, however, the Winterthur Program.
    A last minute note refers to an undergraduate program, including
    two special courses, which has been under revision and which is
    now directed by Charles H. Bohner of the English department.)
UNIVERSITY OF TEXAS (Undergraduate program in planning stages;
    no information on active graduate program.)
WESTMINSTER COLLEGE

AMERICAN STUDIES OUTSIDE THE COLLEGES

Although no systematic efforts have been made in the course of
this survey to accumulate information on American studies outside the
regular offerings of colleges and universities in the United States, a
small handful of such activities has come to our attention. For example,
at least one library and one museum are making use of an American
civilization approach to their own problems. THE LIBRARY COMPANY
OF PHILADELPHIA, in order to exploit its holdings on American subjects, has offered a post-doctoral fellowship to candidates qualified to
work these areas. The announcement clearly implies the desirability
of an interdisciplinary approach. THE WINTERTHUR PROGRAM IN
EARLY AMERICAN CULTURE, which utilizes the facilities of both the
University of Delaware and the Henry Francis duPont Winterthur Museum,
has announced a two-year program "open to college graduates in one of
the humanities, social sciences, or American studies" for graduate
study "in early American arts and cultural history." Candidates for
fellowships are expected to demonstrate "marked ability and exceptional
interest in early American studies, particularly art, history, and literature." This interdisciplinary program is advised as "unparalleled
preparation for careers devoted to curatorship, teaching, research,
journalism, or librarianship." Five graduate fellowships are normally
granted annually for two-year periods.

The CENTER FOR INFORMATION ON AMERICA is in the course
of launching a program in American studies which will have more in
common with the summer refresher programs described above. Under
the presidency of Townsend Scudder, the Center plans eventually for
summer programs for teachers, non-teaching adults, as well as for high
school students. First steps, under a subsidy from the Grant Founda-
dation, call for the development of a syllabus and course-of-study plan

for summer sessions devoted to the presentation of American studies materials to selected high school students. For further information on this activity, see American Studies, III (February, 1958), 1-2. Finally, on the subject of business and American studies, it might be mentioned that the INSTITUTE OF HUMANISTIC EDUCATION FOR BUSINESS EXECUTIVES, developed at the University of Pennsylvania for the Bell Telephone Company of Pennsylvania in 1954 by Morse Peckham, contained an important series of courses on American civilization. This curriculum of the Institute, thus far open only to employees of the sponsoring company, is extremely broad; it utilizes an interdisciplinary approach at many stages and takes up the subject of American civilization as one of its important areas of concentration.

CHAPTER THREE

The American Studies Movement:
A Summary and Analysis

In the pages that follow, some attempt will be made to summarize and to analyze the diverse factors present in American studies activity at the various colleges and universities in this country. The first decade or two of widespread activity in this field has, it is now apparent, raised some continuing questions, provided some recognizable trends. Generalizations encountered here will be based on the writer's own experience in this field and on four other principal sources: (1) previous literature in the field; (2) correspondence and documents leading to the descriptions of specific activity provided in the foregoing chapter of this report; (3) questionnaires provided by responsible individuals at these various institutions under survey, and a statistical analysis of these questionnaires accomplished through the use of an electronic punch card system; and (4) the views and documents expressed and presented at a conference on undergraduate courses and programs in American studies held, with the sponsorship of the Carnegie Corporation, at Washington D. C. in the spring of 1957. For the last-named source, I have relied on the written reports of the recorders for the various sessions. (The recorders were John A. Hague, Stetson University; Wallace E. Davies, University of Pennsylvania; William Jordy, Brown University; John W. Ward, Princeton University; and Murray Murphey, University of Pennsylvania.)

The discussion which follows will be, by and large, self-explanatory. References have been made informally to published materials, but a bibliography has been provided. The one matter which needs explanation at the outset is the use of an "elite" group of institutions with American studies activity as a basis for comparison with the group as a whole. This is not necessarily an elite group in any qualitative sense -- the questionnaire responses out of which it was chosen were not designed to elicit such a judgment. It is an elite group in terms of quantitative success. Because of the varied and general nature of the statistics referring to American studies activity as a whole, some basis for comparison was held desirable; and occasionally the characteristics of this smaller group of institutions whose American studies activities could be described as flourishing have revealed helpful contrasts with the characteristics of the inclusive group. In other situations they only mirror the general picture in microcosm.

Since graduate activities in American studies are relatively limited, the group was chosen and used only with reference to undergraduate programs and courses. The first requisite for membership in the elite, then, was the existence of an undergraduate course or program in American studies. The other requisites all centered around the evidences of quantitative -- and to some extent qualitative -- success in the offerings concerned. Faculty attitude had to be favorable; any courses which were offered had to be reported as popular with the students. If a degree-granting program was offered, it had to have at least ten majors currently, it had to show an increasing enrollment, and it had to be one of the first ten major programs in size at the institution represented. This is not, let it readily be admitted, a set of ideal criteria for establishing an elite group. Any sort of evaluative criteria, however, in the questionnaire responses was scarce, and the need for establishing a basis for comparison proved a real one. Furthermore, those institutions which qualified for this elite group turned out to include a very generous representation of those which, by anyone's standards, would have to be judged as qualitatively elite as well. Although explanation is necessary for the method used in selecting this group, the membership turned out so impressively that the term "elite" can be used without serious misrepresentation.

HISTORY AND EXTENT

An historical account of the growth of American studies has not been an objective of this survey; none of the sources involved are especially suited for this. Of previous speculations on the causes for this development, the accounts by Anthony Garvan, Tremaine McDowell, Richard Shryock, and George Rogers Taylor (see bibliography) seem adequately to cover the many possibilities. To summarize these and other theories, it would appear that the special study of the United States as a civilization by its own citizens can be attributed to three general causes. In the first place there are those external (from the academic) developments during the twentieth century which have tended to make

Americans, always self-conscious, perhaps even more so: the Progressive Era with its "stock-taking" overtones as applied particularly to the political workings of our society; the world wars with their demands for analysis of the ideals standing trial; the critical 20's with that voluble group of intellectual and creative exiles who so ruthlessly subjected the American character and personality to microscopy and dissection; the depression-ridden 30's demanding diagnosis of a way of life which seemed in danger of failing; and finally the post-World War II world in which America, in order to function as model and leader for half the world, has had to explain itself most thoroughly both to itself and to others. Each succeeding decade, heightening in its own way the mood for self-appraisal, has provided a background sympathetic to the problem of examining this civilization.

Secondly, one can mention a trend within the various academic departments during the last half-century which has led not only to the establishment of the United States as a respectable area for study, but also to a broadening of the traditionally narrow and specialized boundaries of the 19th century disciplines so as to allow for a breadth of approach which could begin, at least, to encompass the study of a total culture. Such names as Thorstein Veblen, in economics; Lester Frank Ward, in sociology; and Moses Coit Tyler, in literary history, may serve as examples of such broadening influences during the closing years of the previous century. Other examples, both early and recent, will readily occur to the reader. The historian, during this century, has ever widened his social scope; the chronicler of literature and the fine arts has made notable efforts to relate his subject to its milieu; the anthropologist and sociologist, encouraged by wartime needs, have sharpened their methods for describing contemporary cultures, including their own. Since American studies in the colleges has been, largely, an interdepartmental venture, it no doubt required the broadening of these departmental horizons to foster its inception.

Another academic trend makes up the third causative group, a group which depends on a changing philosophy of education. This direction of change has been toward a return to the concept of general education, a change at least partly due to a reaction against certain forms of departmental and pre-professional specialization. Within the college curriculum, this trend has taken the form, often, of courses or course-groupings designed to augment the student's appreciation of the humanities and social sciences in general. Also, through the influence of those interested in language, literature, and history, as well as sociology and anthropology, area studies have made their way into catalogues and have led inevitably from the remote, in terms of both time and place, to the study of the United States as an area. Thus the concentration of courses around the American "civilization," "culture," "area," or other broad concept, has arisen for a number of possible reasons. On the secondary and even primary levels curricula have been affected by this trend, and the controversial "core curriculum" not only responds to this same impulse but also demands a broader approach to the study of civilization in the public school classroom.

Whatever its causes, American studies in the colleges has (as Robert Spiller proposed and as most of the Washington conferees agreed) grown through two stages so far and may possibly be entering a third. First stirrings were within single departments -- for example in literature departments where resentment was felt against the separation of literature from its environment. From this point, the American "concentration" soon developed with a center on a single discipline (often literary history) buttressed by related work in other fields designed to throw light on an area within the central discipline. This has been called the "one discipline and others" stage. It was probably not until after the second World War that the movement became more truly interdepartmental in nature, relying on roughly equal contributions from at least two departments. History and literature have formed by far the most common combination. But there is now a feeling, and this is perhaps due to the increasingly active participation of the social science disciplines in American civilization courses and programs, that a third stage may be in the making. This stage would center on the study of a civilization as a whole greater than the sum of its parts, but still visibly made up of those parts. Necessary to this stage may be something more than a cooperation between the diverse approaches to the study of civilization, and this something may be nothing less than the achievement of a discipline of American civilization -- a single comprehensive method for examining and organizing the multifold data and phenomena which describe a group of people living in a given place at a given time. This would represent nothing absolutely new, of course, as any anthropologist would attest. But should this concept for the study of American civilization become anywhere nearly so widespread as the present interdisciplinary approach, it would represent a drastic development within this field. (On the subject of an American studies discipline, see especially the articles by James Stone and Henry Nash Smith.)

Figures available from the questionnaires shed little light on such problems as establishing historical causation for the formation of American studies programs. No doubt all the causes mentioned above played their part in this growth which is characterized not by any spurts and retrenching, but rather by a steady increase in an almost geometric ratio. Among the institutions which now participate in undergraduate American studies activity, only one traces its origins prior to World War I. In the 20's, it was joined by two more; and in the 30's by ten. The years of World War II added some sixteen additional colleges to the roster, and the postwar 40's accounted for twenty more. The fifties, so far, have already given birth to some forty-three new programs, counting generally only through 1956-57. As for graduate programs, six were begun in the 30's, eight in the 40's, and five so far in the fifties. Thus the noteworthy element, judging purely from the statistics, would seem to lie not in the particular influence of any force--academic or otherwise--but rather in the existence of a growth of increasing magnitude throughout the last twenty-five years. The only other apparent explanation would lie with the post-World War II emergence of America into world leadership and the effects of this preeminence on the college curriculum.

On the question of departmental initiative for American studies activity, the figures cast doubt on often heard claims for the dominance of one department in the growth of this movement. On the other hand, the figures uphold very pointedly the notion that departments of history and literature have taken the most active part in initiating American studies. Ninety-five institutions responded to the question on departmental initiative; of these, 72 gave credit to the history department and 69 to the English department. Following these in influence, at a respectful distance, are five other departmental interests: political science (31), sociology (22), philosophy and religion (21), the fine arts (19), and economics (18). Other departmental or administrative influences upon the founding of American studies courses and programs appear numerically insignificant. Nor does the situation change appreciably when programs with the earlier dates of origin are examined separately. Of the thirteen institutions where undergraduate activity was reported prior to 1940, for example, the departments of literature and history were each given credit for the original impetus eleven times. Following were political science (6), sociology (4), and philosophy and religion (4). The only noteworthy change from the general picture rests on the disappearance from significance of the fine arts influence in this group, and the substitution of anthropology as a force of equal numerical strength with economics among the minor influences.

To complete the picture of departmental initiative, one must realize the presence of other occasional influences. For example, departments of speech and drama were three times given credit for assisting in the launching of American studies courses or programs. Mentioned twice each were four other departments: music, geography, psychology, and education; and mentioned once each were departments of business and of science history. Furthermore, eight institutions acknowledged that initial impulse was provided for their offering not by any department as such, but by a division, a dean, or by some agency representing the administrative rather than the academic side of the college or university.

So much for how, when, and why American studies activity came alive. The question of the extent and nature of the movement today is one to which the materials at hand lend themselves more readily. This description is based on reports from ninety-five institutions where active courses and/or programs in American studies had existed for at least one year by January, 1958. Other institutions might have been included; some were omitted because of lack of data or due to the recent establishment of the activity in question; some were omitted because of doubt as to the true American studies focus of the course or program. No doubt several institutions have escaped the dragnet of the survey completely. It is probably fair to estimate, however, that these ninety-five institutions represent close to ninety percent of the institutions with active programs or courses in American studies as of 1957.

The nature of the activity in American studies at these ninety-five institutions can be described as follows. In twenty cases this activity is represented only by one or more courses in American civilization. Seventy-two grant the B. A. in American studies; of these, six grant the B. A. and M. A.; three grant the B. A. and Ph. D.; and nine grant all three degrees. One university offers only the doctorate in American studies, and two are here represented only by special programs which neither involve American civilization courses nor lead to American studies degrees. Of the seventy-three institutions which grant one or more degrees in this field, fifty-six offer one or more American civilization special courses. Fifty-four institutions offer undergraduate major programs only, eighteen offer both graduate and undergraduate degrees, and one offers graduate work solely.

A comparison of these figures with earlier surveys in this field and with preliminary stages of the present survey makes for interesting speculation. Tremaine McDowell, the first to offer estimates as to the numerical extent of American studies in the colleges, did his investigating in 1947 and 1948; he found some sixty institutions with undergraduate programs in the field, and a partially overlapping group of fifteen institutions offering graduate work. Also appearing in 1948 was the Crane Report which listed eighty-two institutions offering courses, programs, or both. The preparation of the Crane Report led that committee to comment on the phenomenal growth of this movement in the 40's. At first glance, a comparison of the seventy or eighty institutions reported on in 1948 with the ninety-five listed in the present survey would seem to indicate a less than remarkable growth of American studies during the last decade. To explain this, and at the same time to acknowledge the many institutions (43) which report having started new programs since 1950, one might conclude that while many new programs were doubtless coming into being, many others must have been disappearing.

That this is probably not the case can be seen from a brief account of the progress of the present survey. When the original inquiries were sent around (in 1954-55), no less than one hundred seventy-eight institutions reported activity in American studies. Correspondence pursuant to these replies indicated a "verified" total of ninety-three colleges active in American studies, the list of which was published in American Studies, I (October, 1955), 2-3. Many new offerings have been added even since this time, but painstaking investigation by regional representatives has narrowed the list of institutions with true American studies offerings to the present ninety-five. Thus the lesson seems to be simply that preliminary returns must be severely discounted and that active and time-consuming checking and counter-checking must be accomplished before figures can, with any confidence, be announced. The establishment of criteria for such a nose-counting is difficult, of course, and since the objectives of these various surveys, as well as their methods, have differed considerably, there is also this aspect to be considered. Had either of these previous surveys been conducted in a manner similar to this one, it seems obvious that the total figures would have been considerably less. Many institutions have discontinued their American studies activity; several once-promising programs have become inactive. However -- and direct correspondence with many of the institutions named in earlier surveys confirms this -- the totals offered in the present report seem substantially accurate, and the chronological growth of American studies as represented by the founding dates reported above can be taken to furnish a true measure of consistent growth. It does not seem necessary to make allowances for any unduly large number of abandoned courses or programs.

These ninety-five institutions are scattered throughout the United States with some noticeable variations in the geographical pattern of their distribution. There are fourteen states, for example, where no colleges with American studies activity exist; on the other hand the largest concentration is to be found in states touching on the Atlantic Ocean where fifty-one of the ninety-five institutions are located. New York state has eighteen institutions in this category; following in numerical prevalence are California (7), Massachusetts and Ohio (6 each), and Virginia (5). If American studies has a regional character, though, this must be discovered by relative figures which take into account the frequency of institutions of higher learning as a whole. From this point of view, the picture takes on different dimensions; and the area of the Rocky Mountains and High Plains takes precedence with more than one out of every ten institutions in the region having some sort of American studies activity. Next come the Mid-Atlantic states where one out of every thirteen colleges and universities participates in American studies. After New England (one out of fourteen) comes a sizable drop to the Great Plains area where one out of twenty-two is the ratio; after this come the Midwest and the Farwest where in both cases roughly every twenty-fifth college or university can be counted in American studies. American studies courses and programs occur with least frequency in the South, where but one of thirty colleges participate; and this ratio would be much lower if it were not for the South Atlantic states where the frequency is one out of eighteen. All in all, of the 1,878 institutions of higher learning listed in the 1956-57 Education Directory for the

United States, at least ninety-five have some American studies program: an over-all ratio of more than one in twenty.

An analysis by type and level of the institutions where American studies exists also reveals some differences from the national picture. On the matter of institutional control, for example, these ninety-five colleges mirror the national picture almost exactly in that roughly one-third of them are operated by states or cities; but in the nature of the private control exercised over the remaining two-thirds there is a marked difference. About one-fourth of our colleges, nationally, are private and non-religious; in the American studies group, however, this category makes up practically one half of the total. This means, of course, that colleges controlled by religious groups are represented at less than the national average, by far. Whereas Roman Catholic control is exercised over one out of seven institutions nationally, this is only true of one out of nineteen here. Control by other religious groups is also represented at less than half its nationwide frequency among these institutions. This group is also less than typical in the proportion of primarily technical and teacher-training institutions represented (almost one-fourth, nationally, but only three of the ninety-five) and in junior colleges and strictly undergraduate institutions. Less than one-quarter of American colleges and universities offer the M. A., whereas exactly one-third of these do (although not necessarily in American studies); on the doctoral level the national ratio is one out of ten, whereas thirty-nine of these ninety-five institutions offer the highest degree. Finally, when it comes to education by the sexes, it is apparent that American studies plays favorites with the ladies. Women's colleges represent only one-eighth of the nation's total but one-fifth of the colleges offering American studies. The number of men's colleges here represented is only very slightly less than the national ratio; hence this female favoritism is made up at the expense of the number of coeducational institutions represented.

Comparing the size of institutions offering American studies to the national picture is difficult since junior colleges weight the nation-wide statistics so heavily in the direction of the smaller institutions and since this survey has not included less-than-four-year institutions. Nonetheless, it is apparent that American studies is relatively more prevalent in larger universities, the only exception to this tendency existing in the 1,000-2,500 enrollment category where American studies also has a numerically high proportion. The comparative picture is as follows:

Enrollment	Over-all National %	% of Institutions where American studies is offered
Under 500	56 (approx.)	12 (approx.)
500-1,000	20	15
1,000-2,500	13	27
2,500-5,000	5	9
5,000-10,000	4	18
Over 10,000	2	19
	100	100

Using absolute figures, the typical institution offering American studies could be characterized as: located in New York state, offering at least one advanced degree (though not in American studies), having an enrollment between 1,000 and 2,500, being coeducational and supported from private, non-religious sources. Using relative figures, comparing the institution which has American studies activity with the national composite, one finds American studies predominant in institutions: located in the Rocky Mountain and High Plains region, offering the doctoral degree, having an enrollment over 10,000, being for women only and supported, once again, from private and non-religious sources. Speaking relatively again, one finds American studies offerings notably absent from institutions in the following categories: the South (except the Atlantic coast states), institutions supported from religious sources, institutions primarily for technical and teacher training, coeducational institutions, and institutions with enrollments under 500.

ADMINISTRATION

American studies faculty are sometimes characterized as empire builders replete with administrative retinue and specially staked claims in the generosity of foundationland. Returns from the present survey would substantiate, however, a totally opposite picture. American studies programs exist administratively, for the most part, either within an established framework or on an ad hoc basis. They stand, often, only through the generosity of cooperating departments; courses are taught, programs administered by faculty members in addition to their regular commitments. Only a small fraction of these programs benefit from any outside subsidy whatsoever.

Asked to describe the administrative character of their activity, only five institutions reported the existence of an independent department of American studies. Twenty-seven colleges carry on their offerings within traditional departments (12 in history, 7 in English, 5 in social science departments, and 3 in other departments); the broader sponsorship of a division (usually humanities or social science) accounts for another five. The greatest number by far (40) described their status as that of a quasi-department with control of curriculum, but presumably with control of neither staff nor budget. In addition, twenty institutions reported an even less formal administrative status (a temporary committee or something of this sort), and only two reported the existence of official status for American studies outside the previous university framework. This pattern holds consistently regardless of type or size of institution, with the one qualification that the independent departments are all located in institutions which grant degrees in American studies. Where courses constitute the extent of the offering, then, the activity is more likely to exist within the confines of a conventional department.

For direction of the American studies offering, thirty-six institutions rely on an independent chairman or director (usually representing an interdepartmental committee rather than an established independent department), while twenty subsist under the chairmanship of an established department other than American studies. Most commonly, direction of American studies is attributed to a steering committee composed of departmental representatives (23) or of representatives of the American field in the various interested departments (36). The existence of so many committees made up of departmental representatives is discouraging in the light of the widely held feeling that American studies must be directed by those who are vitally and professionally interested in the American area, rather than simply by representatives of established interests (see especially Robert E. Spiller's paper on this subject). Perhaps these figures should be trusted less than the others rising from the questionnaire; the alternatives here were stated clearly enough on close reading, but it is easy to see how someone checking rapidly through it might misunderstand the distinction between departmental representation and area-of-interest representation. This doubt is raised here not merely as conjecture, but because a close attention to other data presented has frequently made it apparent that the person responding had misunderstood this particular question. However, even if one discounts for some misinterpretation of the question, the results still indicate some considerable variance from the ideal here. In the small college there is a tendency to rely more on the committee, and on the committee representing American interests in particular; whereas in the large, public universities administration is accomplished more often by the independent chairman or director. Within the "elite" group (see above), whereas the administrative character of the offering follows accurately the over-all pattern, the direction of the offering is as follows: independent chairman or director, 6; chairman of traditional department, 8; steering committee of departmental representatives, 2; steering committee of Americanists, 5.

From the fifteen institutions (only three of which are among the "elite" and only eleven of which grant American studies degrees) which report the use of funds from outside the university for American studies activity, a variety of usages emerge. In seven instances, this money was used at least partially to contribute to faculty salaries; in six cases part of the money went toward the purchase of books and other teaching materials. Mentioned five times each were the establishment of special programs outside the regular curriculum and the development of lecture series or other forms of extracurricular activity. Three institutions used their money for scholarships and fellowships, for publications or research projects, or for course experimentation and addition; two institutions used their money for building a physical plant or for conducting a faculty seminar. In only one case were the funds reported as used for administrative operation of the program. It is safe to conclude from these returns that, even in the few cases where outside funds have been used to encourage American studies, the consistent tendency has been to use these monies for strictly academic -- rather than for administrative or even academic-administrative -- purposes.

Whereas at least sixteen institutions report the presence of American studies lectureships of an occasional or part-time nature, only eleven maintain full-time, permanent appointments in this field -- and only four have more than one of these. If at first glance this situation looks bleak indeed for the prospective college teacher in American civilization, it must be remembered that this question was answered from a budgetary point of view and that this point of view represents an important qualification of the data. As this description of administration has already made clear, the great majority of American studies courses and programs are the responsibility, directly or indirectly, of previously existing departments or divisions. Most of these administrative agencies control only curriculum -- not budget; thus any faculty procurement would have to be accomplished in the name of an administrative entity bearing some title other than American studies. In fact, counting the existence of only seven institutions which report financially autonomous American studies activity, it is doubtless surprising not that so few as eleven but that so many as eleven institutions would report positively on the question of full-time faculty in American studies. There can be no doubt that the possibilities for teaching in the American studies field in American colleges is grossly understated by this figure. Nor can there be any doubt, judging from questionnaire reports on faculty assignment to American civilization course work, that the typical faculty picture in this field is that of a person appointed to a traditional department who devotes some fraction of his teaching activity to the field of American civilization. Since the questionnaire was designed to produce a picture of departmental affiliation rather than of graduate training, it is impossible to say what proportion of the faculty engaged in the teaching or

administration of American studies was trained in this field. It is safe
to say, however, that a college teacher hoping to be hired and employed
full-time in American studies has not much width of choice (some eleven
institutions); whereas a college teacher hoping to work part-time in
American studies and part-time in a related department may look toward
a rather large potential area (doubtless over one hundred institutions).

The most important, and the most puzzling, question to be raised
in connection with the administration of American studies involves the
advisability of an independent department. Published views on this subject (see Tremaine McDowell, Richard Shryock, Robert Spiller) insist
that, since American studies represents an interdepartmental approach
to a subject, it would be both inconsistent and unwise to recommend departmental status for it. Robert Spiller has stated, furthermore, that
departmental status implies establishment by administrative fiat (hence
inevitable resentment) rather than the more desirable process of upward
growth, through informal interdepartmental cooperation, from the academic grass roots. In some ways the response to this survey has supported this view.

One question was phrased as follows: "Opinion is divided on the
validity and expediency of erecting full-fledged departments of American
studies. What is your opinion?" Thereupon the responder was given the
space to check yes or no beside two words: "Valid" and "Expedient."
Out of ninety-five possibilities, only thirty-seven checked "yes" as to
validity; only twenty-two checked "yes" as to expediency. When one
considers that the persons making these judgments were responsible for
the American studies activity at their institutions and that this response
therefore represents an "involved" viewpoint, one must conclude that
the total academic attitude toward the department of American studies
is, doubtless, decisively negative. Even when the questionnaire responses are tallied for more limited groups with greater involvement
in American studies, the response, while more favorable to the idea of
the department, is by no means positive. Among the seventy-three
institutions which grant degrees in American studies, for example,
thirty considered the department valid, and fifteen considered it expedient. In the "elite" group of nineteen, nine checked yes for validity,
six for expediency.

The only rebuttal offered by the questionnaire is a tangential one
and refutes only the idea that departmental status engenders uncooper-
ative response. Asked to describe faculty attitudes toward their offerings, fifty-five of the ninety-five checked "favorable," twenty-seven
"mixed," twelve "indifferent," and just one "hostile." Between these
reactions and the existence of American studies departments there is
no negative correlation whatsoever; in fact there is a slight positive one.
The one "hostile" report comes from an institution which, far from
having a department, does not even grant a degree in the field; whereas

those institutions with American studies departments seem blessed by at least as favorable a faculty reaction as those operating with more administrative informality.

The most common objection to departmental status is voiced by Richard Shryock (p. 38 of his article) when he states that this eventuality would hamper the academic development of the program by establishing just one more department with which cooperation would be necessary in order to arrange interdepartmental courses and curricula. Tremaine McDowell (p. 31 of his book) sees the absence of departmental status as a hedge against chauvinism, since all participants in the American studies offering will be forced to identify with established departments where subjects other than American are taught; thus perspective will be, he thinks, automatically retained as long as the institution itself is sane. These and other general statements on this question must lead to philosophical discussions -- such as whether American studies represents primarily an area or a method -- with which this summary is not equipped to deal. The basic assumption most consistently adopted by those who question the value of the American studies department is that the interdisciplinary academic nature of the course or program must be reflected by an interdepartmental administrative status. As an assumption, there is perhaps as much reason to reject as to accept this.

When this subject of departmental validity was discussed, as it was at the Washington Conference, the arguments soon changed from the theoretical to the practical. Many general statements concerning the ideal relationship of American studies activity to the administrative structure of the university were attempted; none of these attempts achieved general concurrence from the Conferees. For example, one person suggested that departmental status was something to be grown into as offerings became more firmly developed; immediately, an opposite opinion was offered -- to the effect that departmental status was most needed at the initiation of an offering when cooperation and budgetary help would be most critically in demand. To refute this, an example was given from the survey returns of an institution where American studies was inaugurated by administrative fiat with full departmental status. The faculty involved, however, considered this unsatisfactory and petitioned for the removal of departmental status. This program began to flourish only when the petition met with success and the program was allowed to continue under a less formal administrative arrangement. Some maintained that departmental status was only fitted for large universities; some maintained that it was particularly necessary in the small college. One favored joint appointment (as in "history and American civilization") for faculty; one favored the inclusion of American studies in a broad "Department of Civilization Study."

An appreciable unity of feeling was achieved only when the chairman of this particular session, David Potter, got down to cases present.

Eight of the conferees, it was established, held doctoral degrees in American civilization, and, although all of them were participating actively in American studies offerings, only four of them held full-time appointments in American civilization. This group, representing in general the younger members of the Conference, supported each other with enthusiastic unanimity on the question of their desire for appointments in their field rather than in related departments. Furthermore, they felt, departmental status for American studies offered them the only sure basis for such appointments and -- once appointed -- for advancement and prestige. The more senior members of the Conference expressed surprise at this positive position and predicted, therefrom, that American studies departments would occur much more widely in the future. Thus it began to seem that the question of departmental validity was not, ultimately, a theoretical one, but a practical one with a clear chronological division. Older teachers in the field, trained in traditional fields, hold secure appointments in relevant departments. They have achieved personal status and are accustomed to working with American studies informally and as somewhat of a sideline to their personal academic development. Younger teachers in the field, however, holding degrees in American civilization, consider this their main line of endeavor and seek an academic structure that will allow them to cultivate this field as their principal academic activity -- a structure that will allow this without penalizing them in terms of advancement. The clearest solution to this demand is, obviously, the department.

Correspondence and questionnaire response to the survey, however, contain material to document the feeling against departmentalization. Time and again one reads reports of programs succeeding only in spite of cooperation withheld by a vital department or failing because of such a lack. Faculty teaching time is reported at a premium, books and materials may be needed, course offerings need to be shored up not only in American civilization but in related areas. Many of these complaints could, apparently, be solved through the establishment of some fiscal and academic autonomy. The point is, however, that those persons feeling the burden of these shortcomings do not turn to departmental status for a solution, as demonstrated by the statistics above. This attitude demonstrates the prevailing strength of the assumption that departmental status is illogical for an interdepartmental program.

The administrative nature of the typical American studies offering can be described as "quasi-departmental" involving control of curriculum but not of budget or staff. (The presence of a budget, of course, may be the crucial item. The experience of at least one institution has shown that a budget can make possible an appropriate staff, course selection, and sense of identity even without departmental status.) It is operated by a director or chairman in close cooperation with a steering committee composed of members of established departments who represent an interest in the American area. The establishment of departmental status is not considered valid, much less expedient. Funds are not forthcoming from outside the institutions and full-time appointments in American studies are not utilized; a favorable faculty attitude toward the program is usually evidenced. This general, typical picture is not significantly altered when institutions are subdivided by type or size or by the nature or extent of their American studies offerings.

UNDERGRADUATE PROGRAMS

Programs in American studies exist for a variety of reasons and purposes; functionally, the great majority of them can be classified in three categories. At the simplest level there is the program which exists merely as a single course offering or as a group of such courses. Nothing approaching a major curriculum is attempted and the purpose of the offering is (in the case most often of the technical or teachers college) to contribute to the achievement of an academic objective completely removed from that of a specialization in the study of American civilization. Where programs of this type exist in a liberal arts setting, the purpose is usually to contribute to the liberal, or "general," education background of the student who majors in a traditional field. Most of the twenty-two institutions covered by this survey which do not grant degrees in American studies fall into this category. This functional type might be called the "service program," since it exists primarily either to serve the general ends of the college or to contribute to the offerings of a curriculum designed, usually, to train a student for a particular career.

A second functional category (exemplified by the American studies offerings at Park College and Princeton University) is more elaborate in that it offers more than a single course and operates in conjunction with some major program in the humanities or social sciences rather than as subsidiary to a professional curriculum. Such a program offers a series of required or recommended courses to be taken along with a major in a traditional, degree granting, department. The student who subscribes to such a curriculum will graduate with a "joint major" (as in political science and American civilization, for example) or will be granted a "certificate" in American civilization to accompany his degree with major in a conventional department. The thought here is to use the American civilization work in order to provide special regional focus to the major work or else to allow for interdisciplinary experience with which to broaden the approach provided by the major discipline. This could be termed a "cooperative" or "correlated" program. If a program developes to this extent, it is usually but a simple further step to the granting of degrees in the American studies field; therefore, programs in this category are relatively rare.

Finally, there are the programs which lead to the granting of the bachelor's degree in an area designated as American studies or American civilization. This category could be termed the "independent program" since it exists as a full-fledged alternative to the conventional major and offers a curriculum of equal academic stature with it. By its existence, it claims the validity of studying American civilization as an area and as a field in which knowledge can be constructively and usefully organized. The form taken by the American studies major is immensely varied; this category is represented by the seventy-two institutions which grant the B. A. in this field. Of these seventy-two, fifty-six offer one or more special courses in American civilization; the remaining sixteen construct a major from course offerings in existing departments. The Washington Conference, recognizing the validity of all three of these functional types as serving genuine needs in their particular institutions, also endorsed the degree-granting program as ideal for institutions where circumstances favor a general liberal arts program of this nature.

To attempt, within this broad functional categorization, any detailed analysis of methodological or pedagogical types which characterize these diverse programs would be an endless project. Certain things can be said, at least, about the theoretical objectives of such programs. Several attempts to phrase a statement of purpose were made at the Washington Conference; the most widely accepted of these was the one proposed by James H. Stone to the effect that American studies programs should center on three objectives: (1) a study of the dynamics of social behavior, (2) a study of the imaginative and expressive experience of the society (some held that this objective should be re-phrased so as to include the study of scientific and technological developments), and (3) the achievement of a formal integrative experience. From one point of view this may simply indicate that a valid program in American studies should include course work of three types: (1) the social sciences and history; (2) literature and the fine arts; and (3) interdisciplinary. Another point of view held that, since the culture concept subsumes all of these three requisites, an American studies program could fulfill itself successfully by adopting this approach as an over-all method. (A decided difference of opinion existed at the Conference between a minority which held that the culture concept provided the approach to the study of civilization, and the majority which held that it represented only one of many valid and useful approaches. Whether this should be the case or not, it is true that no undergraduate program has organized itself so as to utilize the culture concept as the integrative method from first to last; therefore this debate belongs more to the question of course organization and over-all philosophy and will be treated in this connection below.) The question of valid aims for a program in American studies was the subject of considerable discussion at the Conference, but it never proceeded beyond the above statement or beyond the above dichotomy of viewpoint.

Questionnaire response also provides some material on this subject via the following question which allowed room for an answer of paragraph length: "Please make a brief statement embodying the aims of your offerings. Why do you think American Civilization...is valid as a distinct offering in a college or university?" Perhaps surprisingly, answers to this query turned solidly in the direction of methodology; fifty-two (by far the largest single category) of the ninety-four who replied emphasized the importance of the interdisciplinary approach as a principal factor -- usually for its own sake, but often as an antidote to the overspecialization felt to be present in more traditional approaches. Also using methodological criteria were the eight who considered the distinctiveness of their programs to lie in a utilization of the culture concept as an approach to learning. The second largest trend in these answers involved the endorsement of American studies as a program offering a broad, liberal training (not necessarily interdisciplinary, but at least involving a wide range of subjects in the liberal arts) as opposed to the more specialized programs with career objectives. Contrariwise, eleven answers contained support of American studies as training for specific careers. Twenty-seven answers stressed the advantages of American studies programs for presenting America's heritage (an additional six specifically stressed the presentation of foreign contributions to American civilization), whereas eighteen emphasized the opportunity afforded the student to know better himself and his environment, and thirteen seconded this contemporary focus by stressing the need to know American better on account of her role in world affairs. Fifteen institutions stressed American studies for citizenship training (this was particularly the case when foreign students were largely involved); two thought their programs distinguished by a regional approach. Only two responses contained any hint of chauvinistic or doctrinaire points of view.

A related question requested an explanation for student motivation in enrolling in American studies offerings where such were not compulsory. The alternatives provided were "nationalism," "liberal education," and "intellectual curiosity." The first was checked three times (out of the 78 responses to this question), the second fifty-seven, and the third fifty-four times. A number of other motivations were suggested, but none with sufficient frequency or consistency to be worth mentioning. Most people were satisfied with the alternatives presented, and most of them, obviously, checked both liberal education and intellectual curiosity. It appears from these two questions that American studies carries, at least in the minds of those who operate these programs, two principal connotations. One is conservative and involves a return to the type of broad, liberal education which characterized the better liberal arts colleges before the wave of specialization and career-preparation took over so many of our institutions of higher learning. The other is experimental and rests on a dedication to exploit the intellectual curiosity of alert students in the direction of new approaches to the study of civilization, usually interdisciplinary in nature.

More important than an estimate of aims and motivations, perhaps, is an account of how these aims are carried out in terms of curricula in American studies. Implicit in both the definition of the ideal program proposed at the Washington Conference and in the response to the questions reported above, is a need for the provision of some integrative interdisciplinary experience. Since many of these programs developed out of course offerings already existing in conventional departments, which were then collected and listed in such a way as to provide an American studies major "by addition," this acknowledgement of the necessity for the special integrating course is not without its point. Without such a course, the student is expected to assimilate and organize the diverse materials and approaches offered by this miscellany of courses into a meaningful pattern on his own initiative. In such a program, to put it simply, the student is being asked to do something for which his curriculum provides no example. The Conference expressed itself strongly to the effect that this did not provide a reasonable and legitimate educational experience; and that any American studies program should include, therefore, at least one course in which the student would be provided with some exemplification of how this organization and integration might be accomplished. The most logical, as well as the most usual, place for such a course occurs in the undergraduate's senior year. If a second course can be afforded, it should come near the beginning of the curriculum, either in the first or second years, and may thus be considered a prerequisite to the major. An intermediate course, it was proposed, might also be desirable but would not be so essential as the other two, the one of which sets the pattern for integration and allows for the profitable assimilation of materials as the student progresses through his curriculum, and the second of which acts as capstone to his undergraduate career by pulling together these materials into a meaningful synthesis relating to American civilization as a whole. Although the evidence of the survey indicates a pattern whereby the senior course is typically the first to appear, followed by the lower division course and finally by the intermediate course or tutorial, the Conference indicated that this pattern was not to be considered in any way an ideal, but that each program should attempt to develop its offerings to the full range in whatever manner proved best suited to local conditions. (A more detailed discussion of courses will be included below.) By way of relating the ideal to the actual, the survey shows that thirty-two of the institutions granting undergraduate degrees (72) offer a single special American civilization course; ten offer two such courses, and fourteen offer three or more.

Aside from the special course, the major program in American studies depends on selected offerings from conventional departments. The Conference recognized only two staples here -- a course in American intellectual history and a course in American literature -- and the response to the questionnaire bears out this estimate. Of the sixty-nine institutions which furnished information under the heading of fields in which course work was required of undergraduate American studies majors, sixty-six listed history and sixty-four listed literature. Other areas lagged significantly behind these two in the following order: philosophy (34), foreign history or civilization (29), political science (25), art (25), sociology (17), economics (13), religion (12), and a social science option (10). Still less frequently mentioned fields included architecture, history of science and technology, music, geography, anthropology, a humanities option, psychology, speech, and education. This response also tends to support, at least slightly, another generalization proposed at the Conference, namely that American studies programs were heading in the direction of a history-social science orientation rather than in a literature-fine arts direction. If these required fields of study can be taken as generally indicative of this emphasis, then one finds the ratio at 171 to 101 in favor of the general field of history-social science over the general field of literature and the arts. The third area of philosophy and religion would be represented in this ratio by the number 46. Furthermore, in cases where a choice of concentration within the American studies major is allowed, a preference on the part of the students is reported for history (29) over literature (18). The occurrence of other areas here is negligible.

In many colleges the first two years of the undergraduate are occupied with general requirements outside the major. This is not true of some fifty-five institutions with undergraduate American studies majors, and in these instances the course requirements during the freshman and sophomore years for prospective American studies majors turned out as follows: American history (41), American literature (27), foreign civilization (18), political science (17), American civilization (11), a social science option (9), sociology (6), philosophy (5), art (4), economics (4), religion (3), science (3), speech (3), geography (2), music (2), psychology (1), architecture (1), and a humanities option (1). Seventy institutions listed upper division requirements for the American studies major, and the frequency of occurrence in this category can be summarized as: American literature (50), American history (47), American studies seminar (35), American civilization integrating course (24), political science (21), philosophy (20), foreign civilization (14), art (13), economics (13), sociology (11), music (6), a social science option (6), geography (5), architecture (4), religion (4), education (3), a humanities option (2), anthropology (1), commerce (1), and psychology (1). These statistics demonstrate three important items: that requirements for the major occur much more fully in the final two years, that special integrating courses in American civilization are offered with much greater frequency as upper division requirements; and that, whereas American history and literature are both generally required, it is more common to place the history requirement in the first two years and the literature requirement in the last two years.

The matter of the number and arrangement of specific course requirements for the American studies major raises an important question involving the philosophy behind such programs. This question, in its most simplified terms, can be stated as follows: should there be, at a given institution, one recommended list of course requirements which will constitute the desired curricular experience for all majors; or, must each student be allowed to construct for himself an individualized pattern of courses suited to his own particular needs and background. On the one hand is a fixed series of requirements or narrow alternatives which insure a desired coverage of materials and approaches. On the other hand is a loose, permissive arrangement which depends on the adviser's initiative for any logic that may be drawn from an arrangement of the general course offerings available. Responses to the questionnaire indicate that both types of major programs are in operation and that the latter is more common. Fifty-five (of 72) institutions make specific course requirements of the major student during his first two years; seventy of the seventy-two require specific courses during the final two years. However, beyond such "staple" requirements as American literature and history and special American civilization courses, very few specific listings occur at any level. The most frequently required course, not counting these staple offerings, occurs only eighteen times during the first two years; during the last two years, twenty-one examples may be found for a set course requirement outside the central group. Thus, although the listing of fixed obligations for the major student in American literature, history, and civilization is the rule, it is rare that anything approaching a full curriculum is set forth for the major student. Evidence as to the advantages or disadvantages of this arrangement is contradictory. Some institutions report that the attraction of the American studies major for students lies in this very flexibility which enables a curriculum to be "tailor-made" for the individual student. Other examples are available of programs which were unsuccessful (because students were unable to discover just what the American studies major comprised) until alterations were made in the direction of tightening the curriculum, allowing less individual freedom, and listing a greater number of specific course requirements.

When the question of the "loose" versus the "fixed" program was raised at the Washington Conference, the reaction was tangential. It was recommended that a fixed group of courses, including if possible a special interdisciplinary American civilization course, be required at the outset (freshman or sophomore year) and at the termination (senior year) of the major program. The principal problem was recognized as lying with the selection of intermediate courses which would lead to an organized and constructive approach to the study of the civilization. Some suggestions were made as to how·course groupings could be established (as by discipline or area) wherein the students would be required to cover a minimum of two approaches (as between history, literature and the fine arts, the social sciences, and philosophy). None of these systems met with any general approval, however, and the discussion of this point ended with a strong recommendation that the adviser pay particular attention to the selection of courses so as to provide sufficient depth of experience for the student. On the one hand, then, it seems difficult to recommend between the individualized and the formalized program in principle; and the variables springing from the nature of the institution and its staff will no doubt dictate the proper response. On the other hand, however, sentiment clearly favors a certain rigidity of curriculum in the freshman and senior years, especially if the fixed requirements center around one or more special American civilization courses. One important principle to be recognized, certainly, is that each individual student's program -- whether it conform to a general set of requirements or not -- have a structure, a coherence and a rationale of its own.

Whatever the degree of rigidity or permissiveness, most (53 of 72) institutions chose the same phrase to describe the nature of their undergraduate major program: "Interdepartmental or interdivisional major including humanities, social sciences, and history." Many other alternatives were offered but none was checked more than half a dozen times. Individual departmental sponsorship still plays a great part in American studies programs, but apparently this sponsorship is more administrative than curricular in its effects. Six programs were described as English majors: three with minors in history, three with minors in the American area; eight programs were described as history majors: four with minors in English and four with minors in the American area. Seven programs were described as double majors, most commonly English and history. Other single or joint departmental sponsorships accounted for nine instances. The phrase, "interdepartmental major in social science" was preferred by four institutions, whereas its counterpart in the humanities was checked three times. Only five institutions felt that their programs were so individualized that they could be described under none of the headings provided. The characterization of the major by one of these descriptions did, however, seem something of a problem for many who responded to the questionnaire. A check of the statistics reported here will indicate that many times more than one phrase was selected, the point of this being that most programs appeared capable of definition only as a broad, interdepartmental effort, involving some participation from the humanities as well as the social sciences. In order to give this general description more meaning, the respondant frequently checked, also, one of the more narrowly descriptive phrases; hence, in many cases, one would have to combine answers in order to sense the real nature of the major.

In case the phrase "interdepartmental or interdivisional major including humanities, social sciences, and history" was checked, the respondant was also asked to indicate whether or not the major also required "a concentration of work in one traditional field as well as a distribution across several." Only fourteen (of 53 possible) institutions checked this affirmatively which may have some significance in the light of the carefully expressed proviso (at the Washington Conference) that the American studies major need furnish some definite assurance of curricular "depth." There are, of course, many ways of providing such depth; and it is apparent from this response that those responsible for the American studies majors feel that this depth must, generally, be provided outside the traditional pattern of departmental concentration.

Another important question on which the questionnaire throws some light involves the degree of difficulty of the typical American studies major. At the Washington Conference a tendency was recognized in several institutions leading to the establishment of American studies as a virtual honors program. Better-than-average students may be more readily attracted to American studies because of its novelty and the aura of experiment that is often associated with it, because of the relative freedom of course choice that often accompanies it, because of the amount of individual attention which is sometimes provided the American studies major, because of the extra work frequently demanded, or because of special scholarships or prizes awarded. Some of these factors might also attract the average or below-average student, but the sum total of their appeal is toward the superior student. Although this tendency toward making the American studies major a small and select one was recognized, it was not necessarily applauded. Although such a status may be the only feasible one in some institutional situations, it was felt that a general trend to equate American studies with superior students only would be -- to a large extent -- to defeat the nature of the movement as a force in undergraduate curricula.

The questionnaire offers evidence as to the prevalence of this trend in a number of ways. Slightly over half of the institutions concerned, for example, reported that the course load required of American studies majors was roughly equal to that required of majors in conventional fields. Only one institution reported the American studies major to be less demanding than others, and the remainder (34 out of 72) testified that a greater hour load accompanied their major program. Twenty-six institutions require a special grade average for their American studies majors; thirty-nine do not. Forty-four institutions felt their American studies majors to represent the institutional average as to intellectual ability; forty-one found their majors above average (none reported below average). From these responses it appears that the American studies major, if not virtually an honors program, at least tends in that direction. The split is nearly even between the tendency to characterize this major as a program for exceptional students and the tendency to regard it as on a level with the other college programs.

The question of the size of the typical American studies program bears on this question also, but so many other factors are here involved that this characteristic cannot be taken as direct evidence. From sixty-nine institutions, figures were made available covering the average size of the major during the last five years; these reports may be tabulated as follows:

Average size of American studies major during last five years	Number of institutions reporting in this category
Less than 6 students	27
6 - 10 students	18
11 - 15 students	7
16 - 20 students	6
21 - 30 students	4
31 - 40 students	2
41 - 50 students	None
51 - 100 students	2
Over 100 students	3

As a comparison, all seventy-two institutions with undergraduate programs reported on their most recent enrollment (1957 in most cases):

Most recent annual enrollment in American studies major	Number of institutions reporting in this category
No students enrolled	5
Less than 6 students	24
6 - 10 students	13
11 - 15 students	6
16 - 20 students	3
21 - 30 students	8
31 - 40 students	5
41 - 50 students	2
51 - 100 students	4
Over 100 students	2

As to comparative strength of the major, only six institutions reported American studies among the first five, eleven among the second five, eight among the third five, six among the fourth five, and thirty-one among the last five. Thirty-three reported no major change in enrollment during the last five years; eight reported a decreasing enrollment; and twenty-eight reported an increasing enrollment. In spite of this definite trend of the major either to expand or to hold its own, the typical major remained fairly constant in size due to the entry into the field of newly established programs with their accompanying small enrollments. Thus, the average program over the last five years had an annual enrollment of some 17 students; whereas the most recent figures indicate an increase only to 19, roughly. The typical, or "mean" program continues to operate in the 5-10 bracket as it has over the last five years. While these programs seem definitely to be increasing in size, they are still well within the bracket which could characterize them as operations designed for -- or at least attracting -- the few rather than the many, although these "means" and "averages" may be more realistically appreciated as the balancing of many small programs against a few very large ones.

Other characteristics of undergraduate programs may be reported here as a sort of miscellany, before bringing this section to a close. Several of these programs sponsor extra-curricular activities of which the most popular variety takes the form of public lectures (at thirty-two institutions) followed by film series (16), exhibitions (12), student organizations and projects (12), and concerts (10). Changes are usually necessary in the curricular side of the program once established; most frequently these changes involve adding or modifying courses (28 reports of this), revising requirements (18), altering the administrative framework (6), or some other of a variety of miscellaneous adaptations. Only fifteen reported that no changes had been necessary. Courses added, not counting special American civilization courses, to the required or recommended major came from the following departments: the fine arts (in 17 instances), history (14), philosophy and religion (13), literature (7), foreign civilization (4), the history of science (3) and a miscellany of other sources mentioned no oftener than once. These data in no way characterize the emphasis of the major since there is no fixed relationship between the type of course required at the initiation of the major, on the one hand, and the type of course later found beneficial. The fact of programs "moving" so as to include more of the materials of the fine arts, however, is at least apparent. The institutions were also asked to indicate what sort of courses might be needed so as to achieve a desired curriculum in American studies within the general curriculum. The remarkable thing here was that so many respondents (31) failed to rise to this bait at all; where suggestions were made, they followed the following pattern: fifteen indicated the need for courses in fine arts, fifteen also in philosophy and religion; six in history, the history of science, or sociology and anthropology; four in folklore; three in literature or economics. Whereas it will be remembered that American studies programs were relatively more frequent in women's colleges than in any other type, by sex, it can be reported -- perhaps to the contrary -- that within coeducational institutions the typical undergraduate major is male rather than female by a ratio of 13 to 11. Other institutions (37) reported no noticeable distribution by sex.

The typical American studies undergraduate major, by way of summary, offers a program leading to a degree and thus falls into the "independent" rather than the "cooperative" or "service" category. It aims for a broad, liberal education through an interdisciplinary experience and seeks to accomplish this objective with an interdepartmental or interdivisional program including the humanities, social sciences, and history. Requiring little in the way of specific courses beyond American literature and history, the typical program assures the student of the opportunity to integrate his interdepartmental curriculum through a special course in American civilization, usually at the senior level. The program is individualized to suit the needs, interests, and background of the student and involves little specialization in the conventional sense. Requiring a course load equal to or greater than the conventional major, the American studies program attracts students equal to or above the institutional average. Established since World War II, or even probably since 1950, the program has an increasing enrollment but still operates, typically, with less than ten students (the mean is between 6 and 10; the average is in the high teens). If changes have been made since the establishment of the curriculum, they probably involve course offerings and probably represent a move toward covering such areas as the fine arts and philosophy which were not a part of the original set of recommended or required courses.

The elite group reflects the over-all picture quite accurately, except that by definition the programs here represented occupy a more central place among the major programs at their respective institutions. Programs here too are individualized and involve few requirements beyond history and literature of the United States. They were, as a group, founded earlier, the enrollments are larger, and they offer more courses (especially on the introductory level) in American civilization per se. Since the enrollment is larger, the students approach more closely the institutional average in intellectual abilities; still, nearly half rate their majors as above average. The interdisciplinary advantages of the program are heavily stressed, but so also (more than typically) are such factors as the contemporary application of the curriculum and the pertinence of foreign contributions to America. Thus the elite program tends, at the same time, to be more contemporary and less provincial than the more broadly typical one. Otherwise, this special picture reveals nothing beyond the general one.

UNDERGRADUATE COURSES

It has been impossible, of course, to discuss undergraduate programs in American studies without discussing undergraduate courses in American studies; the reader should therefore refer to the preceding section for much pertinent information on this general subject. Course offerings represent, in some ways, the most positive expression of the American studies movement; in some twenty institutions, the course offerings are the extent of the program. Of the seventy-two institutions which grant the B. A. in American studies, fifty-five offer special courses as well. Of the ninety-five institutions surveyed, forty-six offer one undergraduate course, thirteen offer two courses, and sixteen offer three or more. One institution offers eight undergraduate American civilization courses, one offers six, three offer four, and eleven offer three courses. Thirteen institutions offer two undergraduate courses, and forty-six institutions offer a single course. Thus, through the questionnaire, seventy-five institutions have contributed testimony as to the existence of some hundred-fifty undergraduate American civilization courses, and information in some detail on roughly one hundred of these courses has been electronically coded and made statistically available.

This rather large amount of information lends itself to organization in a number of useful ways. One could follow the functional definition of programs established above and consider, separately, the courses existing as part of the "service," cooperative," or "independent" programs. The information divides itself, however, not according to the general environment of the course offering, but rather according to the specific purpose for which the particular course is designed. From this point of view there are perhaps five functional types of undergraduate course which can be recognized, and which can be said to exist to any measurable extent.

(1) The most obvious type of undergraduate course is the straightforward introductory survey which has as its purpose the coverage of the materials of American civilization. It may exist as a counterpart to a "Western Civilization" course, or it may compete with or replace a survey in American history, or possibly American literature. Rather than as training for American studies majors, this type of course exists for the benefit of the college as a whole and, more often than not, furnishes at least an alternative way of fulfilling some general requirement within the social science-humanities area. Typically, it is arranged chronologically and is conducted by a single individual using the lecture method. The only surprising thing, perhaps, is that it has not -- generally -- found its way into the first two years of the college curriculum where it would be most appropriate; but, like American studies courses in general, has been taken primarily by juniors and seniors. There are many explanations for the fact that so called "introductory" courses in

American civilization wind up being taken by upper division students, but one of the most prevalent rests on the difficulty of breaking into the relatively fixed lower division requirements which are in force at so many colleges. The established courses which have been designed to satisfy these fixed requirements are guarded, often jealously, by those whose vested interests may be at stake; and it is often difficult for those responsible for the new American civilization offerings to find places for them as alternatives, even, among the general requirements for the first two years. So it is not unusual to find the introductory courses in American civilization taken by students as electives during their last two years, the time when elective hours are usually more ample in the student schedule.

Concerning the American civilization survey course, the most pertinent question is not related to the level of offering, but rather to the advisability of offering such a course at all. Those present at the Washington Conference expressed themselves firmly in the negative on this point. Survey courses, it was felt, should be left to the established departments where, even though the necessary chronological scope may pose problems, at least there does not exist the added complication of attempting to combine materials from a number of areas. True, three thousand years of Western civilization, as represented not only in science and politics but also in literature and fine arts, is customarily presented in two terms of normal college course work. Here an historical framework is consistently adopted. If the American civilization survey is to contribute anything new to the curriculum from a methodological point of view, it must -- so the Washington Conferees felt -- curb any ambitions to cover, within a single course, all of American civilization; it must attempt instead to limit materials to be covered and thereby allow for more penetration and experimentation.

(2) It is this quality -- of depth and experimentation -- which functionally differentiates the selective introductory course from the survey type; and it was to this functional type that the Washington Conference turned its attention most seriously and at greatest length. Several specific courses were discussed. In the end, it was apparent that the Conferees were interested in and impressed by only two general types of selective introductory undergraduate courses in American civilization. One of these types, exemplified especially by offerings at Princeton, could be called a thematic course since it depends for its organization on the collection of materials around a special theme, in the case of Princeton, "individualism." (The Princeton introductory course is described in a pamphlet which may be had upon request: John William Ward, The Special Program in American Civilization at Princeton (Princeton, 1957). This represents not only one of the more distinguished course types, but also the most popular. Some 75% of American civilization courses are listed as organized around one or more

themes or topics, rather than around a fundamentally chronological plan. Any number of examples of themes could be furnished, all of them tending to point the course in the direction of one set of materials or disciplines more than another. The great advantage of this organization for an interdisciplinary course lies in the possibility of tracing a theme, let us take "individualism" as an example, throughout many diverse areas -- in this case political theory, religion, philosophy, creative expression, and many other areas. Furthermore, this useful interdisciplinary experience can be accomplished unobtrusively by directing attention to the theme itself rather than to the process of searching through a number of traditionally unrelated compartments for the materials and approaches with which to describe the theme. As an introductory course, it is probably important that the interdisciplinary experience be achieved with as little selfconsciousness as possible -- particularly since the introductory course is usually intended not only for future American studies majors but for undergraduates at large.

A variation of this general type, with some important differences (see George Rogers Taylor's article, "Teaching the Art of Decision Making") is represented by the problems course. Here (examples at the Conference were drawn principally from Yale and Amherst) one finds the theme phrased as an issue (Should one have voted for Bryan or McKinley? Was Jackson or Biddle right? See the Problems in American Civilization series, Boston: D. C. Heath.) which is then pursued in a manner similar to the theme except that of course the directions of pursuit are more sharply bisected and tend also to involve more specific problems. (Several texts and source books represent the problem approach to the study of American civilization; one of them grew out of the Yale course which was also discussed at some length at the Washington Conference. For a discussion of these and other types of materials related to the teaching of American history and civilization see W. E. Davies' article listed in the bibliography.) The same virtue of involving the student unobtrusively and constructively in an interdisciplinary experience pertains just as notably to this variation of the thematic course; also, much has been claimed for this type of course because it involves the student and forces him through a process of decision-making which aids him in coming to understand not only his civilization but, eventually, himself. The problems approach is more readily suited to the materials of political science, political and economic history, than it is to other areas, particularly creative expression. There are some notable exceptions to this rule, but it is generally true that these courses and the texts which pertain to them are slanted, from a departmental point of view, toward the areas mentioned. The more general type of thematic course, where issues are not necessarily involved, need not direct itself in this way.

The second type of selective introductory course which interested the Washington Conferees was discussed with the single example of Anthony Garvan's course at the University of Pennsylvania. This type, the culture concept course, is not nationally prevalent (only eleven courses mention utilizing this method of organization even partially) and the example furnished may be unique in the faithfulness with which this approach is pursued. Based on the methods some anthropologists have proposed for studying a civilization, the course in question drew specifically on the Human Relations Area File (published by the Institute of Human Relations, Yale University) in order to establish categories and criteria for arranging descriptive data concerning a particular culture-- in this case, American from 1650 to 1950. Primary materials were selected and presented in such a way as to provide for a rounded picture, in anthropological terms, of the cultural group. The Conferees expressed themselves as greatly impressed by this course, at least as an experiment in teaching with no small degree of originality. Its attractiveness lay in its subscription to a method of organization which allows -- at least by its own terms -- for complete assimilation of data into a fixed descriptive outline. There is no doubt some additional appeal in the use of primary sources -- paintings, diaries, furniture, community plans -- particularly for the undergraduate. The disadvantages of the course are roughly the same as those of the cultural approach in general. Some point to particular weaknesses, such as the inability of this approach to preserve the unusual products of the creative imagination as any more than another bit of evidence pertaining to the culture. Others believe that the apparent ability of this concept to arrange all descriptive data may be only illusory. One can, in short, describe this general method as controversial; but one cannot ignore the attractiveness of using this device to organize teaching in the field of American civilization -- at least this seemed to be the attitude of those who joined in discussing the culture concept course.

The only other type of selective introductory course which might be mentioned is the period course involving a single decade or some limited, intensive chronological approach. If the survey course is to be objected to, one logical way out might simply involve abbreviating the time period covered in order to enlarge the disciplinary scope. Logical as this may seem, it is apparently not effective. Less than 4% of the courses described make use of this method of organization, and the subject did not even come up at the Washington Conference.

(3) A third functional type of course involves an intermediate approach, one that functions as a type of training for the major between the introduction to the subject and the final exposure to it. As indicated under the discussion of programs, the intermediate course is the most rare and the last to develop within a program. Some participants at the Washington Conference doubted the necessity for such a course at

all. At the present time, when so many "introductory" courses are being taken by juniors or even seniors, it is perhaps difficult to imagine finding a spot in the curriculum for an intermediate course. Theoretically, however, there is no reason to think that such a course could not have both a meaningful place and an important function. If, as seems at least to be the recommendation, American civilization courses are to distinguish themselves by their experimental methods and by their attention to selected themes rather than to a total coverage of materials, how is the major student to be assured a coverage of the principal events, works, and ideas in his field? Many of the introductory and senior courses alike ignore this problem. In discussing the program it was admitted that the greatest weakness occurred in those intermediate years when selections had to be made from courses offered by conventional departments which did not always suit precisely the objectives of the American studies curriculum. Very few institutions have faced up to this problem -- very few have had the chance to, for that matter, due to the dislocation of the introductory course -- but at some institutions at least (Barnard College of Columbia University is the best example) intermediate instruction has been provided in terms of reading lists and tutorials based on them. Sometimes the senior seminar undertakes this same task of covering the major readings in American civilization, but there seems little doubt that some assurance is needed of the student's familiarity with at least a minimum of works in the field; it also seems clear that such seminar topics as research and discussion of method, could be much more efficiently achieved if the basic readings had been taken care of at an intermediate level and if, therefore, all students possessed at least some common ground for discussion.

Aside from these tutorials (which are a part of the institutional pattern rather than an innovation brought about by American studies in many cases) no general class of intermediate course can be discussed. If a program features a single course, it is usually an upper division integrating course meant as a summary experience for the major. If the institution has two courses, the second one is typically aimed at the problem of introducing the student to selected themes or problems in American civilization. If further courses exist, they represent further elaborations of the introductory course pattern, usually. Only rarely is an intermediate, or a second summary course provided.

(4) Some American studies programs have recognized the need for an upper division integrating course, conducted by lecture or by lecture-discussion and devoted to one of the selective approaches to the study of the civilization. So far this functional category has been largely hypothetical since, as already mentioned, the introductory courses are as yet so frequently relegated to the last two years of the curriculum. What has been said under category #2 above (the selective introductory course) can apply very well to this category, at least for the present.

As upper division integrating courses develop, however, they will be designed more for the major in American studies than for the general student body; they will therefore be more highly experimental, more self-conscious in the exposure to the interdisciplinary process, and less dedicated to any fixed content coverage.

(5) One fundamental requirement for an American studies program is an integrating experience, an opportunity for the major to assimilate and coordinate the various knowledge relevant to American civilization which he will have accumulated in his curriculum. For the major student, the most common method of providing this experience is the special seminar in American civilization. The questionnaires furnish evidence of the existence of at least thirty-nine such seminars, with information in some detail on thirty-two of them. Limited usually to seniors majoring in the field, these courses are distinct from the integrating course in their use of the seminar method, their reliance on student participation in the form of both discussion and individual research.

Special emphasis is placed on the contributions of the various disciplines to the study of American civilization. To this end specialists from several departments are often invited to participate, and course organization is often resolved simply by taking up these various contributions one after another. The most common organization for the seminar, though, is once again the topical, frequently limited to one major theme or to a small number of selected themes. The instructor in charge is, more often than is the case with other courses, affiliated with an American studies department or at least trained in the field of American civilization. Although seminars exist only where there are formal programs, they are occasionally opened to students outside the major, and in such cases they have proven to be quite popular as electives, according to questionnaire returns. Much that is true about the special seminar is also true about other American civilization courses, but the seminar can be distinguished by its high degree of experimentation, its susceptibility to cooperative teaching (there is room for caution here lest the variety represented by a stream of guest lecturers cause the course to get out of hand and end by contributing confusion rather than integration), and its ever-changing contextual focus which causes most of these courses to be described as "varying from term to term" in content and organization.

Opinion expressed at the Washington Conference stressed the necessity for an upper division integrating course and endorsed the seminar as the desirable type. The introductory and the senior course, it was felt, should be carefully coordinated both as to subject matter and as to method; if possible, both courses should be planned and taught by persons trained in American civilization. The difference between the two could be stated as one of degree rather than of type, with the upper division course representing a more intense and specialized experience. No absolute objection was sustained against the use of several instructors in the seminar, so long as the course maintained a clear direction and the student was not left with a bewildering variety of opinions rather than with a solid framework on which to build his own intellectual synthesis.

As with programs, courses in American studies exist in varied settings and for a variety of reasons, not all of which can be covered by any general statements or categories. The foregoing discussion should prove most usefully organized for those interested in the function of courses and their interrelationships within the undergraduate major program in American studies. On the other hand, where the question involves the existence of courses as separate from a formal program, the situation can be covered almost completely by the first two categories discussed above. Other functional categories will occur to anyone who reads through the descriptive essays pertaining to the specific institutions; but, except for those mentioned above, the instances supporting these categories are too rare to merit discussion.

To summarize the total picture presented by American civilization course offerings will prove less helpful than the foregoing discussion to anyone interested in the internal problems of American studies curricula. On the other hand, the total statistics may help to give a general picture and thus to aid in furthering a definition of the American studies movement. Practically everyone responsible for these courses checked as their purpose the introduction of a new approach to the study of American civilization. In about 70% of the cases, this new approach was expected to benefit the institution at large, rather than apply only to the training of students majoring in the field. Slightly more than half of all American studies courses offered are open to seniors, about one-third are open to juniors, less than one-tenth are open to sophomores, and one-fifteenth are open to freshmen. These courses are organized as follows: almost one-third as selected topics or problems arranged chronologically; almost one-fourth based on individual research, one-sixth on single topics or themes; one-twelfth on the culture concept; and smaller fractions on such bases as the great books approach, selected topics without chronology, the examination of the assumptions of the various disciplines. These data will prove misleading unless it is borne in mind that more than one of the methods of organization indicated is often employed in the same course. The figures do give, of course, a true picture of the proportions of emphasis in organizing American civilization courses.

The same is true of the teaching method, more than one technique often being used in the same class. The discussion method prevails in about 60 per cent of the cases, with discussions led by various specialists being slightly more common than discussions led by a single instructor. In classes where lecturing predominates (about 40%), the practice of inviting various specialists is, once again, slightly more prevalent than that of relying on a single lecturer. According to departmental affiliation, these courses are staffed (in approximate percentages) as follows: literature, 23%; history, 22%; political science, 11%; anthropology and sociology, 8%; American studies, 8%; the fine arts, 8%; philosophy and religion, 8%; economics, 6%; science, 2%; education, 1%; others, 3%. A corresponding emphasis in the subject matter presented in these courses might be evidenced had the questionnaires provided similarly for responses; however, some categories required only check marks from the responder, whereas others demanded write-ins, thus heavily favoring the former. Where the subject was listed, the following response can be noted: 90% of the courses included both history and literature; 84% included philosophy; 76%, religion; 66%, art; 60%, architecture; 58%, history of science and technology; and 51%, music. Where it was necessary for the responder to write in departmental sources, the indications were as follows: 33% included sociology; 22% included political science; 22%, economics; 11%, anthropology; 11%, psychology; 8%, education; 7%, science; and 5%, geography. Had equal representation been provided all relevant departments on the questionnaire, it seems likely that the proportions would have corresponded more exactly to those representing departmental faculty participation or departmental course requirements.

Where American civilization courses were not required, the responder was asked to judge whether or not such courses had proved popular with students. Fifty answers were affirmative on this question, as opposed to eight negative. Space was also provided for estimates as to the cause of either condition, but the only comment to emerge with any recognizable consistency had to do with the importance of the American civilization course as a vital part of a curriculum other than American studies. Even this answer occurred but nine times, so it would be dangerous to propose any explanation at all for what appears to be an unusual popularity enjoyed by American civilization course offerings.

Aside from their popularity, perhaps the only unusual aspect to emerge from this study of American civilization undergraduate courses is their prevalence as upper rather than lower division courses. They include materials from a great many sources, mainly literature and history followed by philosophy, religion, and the fine arts. The social sciences seem under-represented, which may be the fault of the questionnaire. Course organization is generally thematic and teaching takes the form of discussion often led by more than one instructor. The courses are staffed by literature and history department members, joined by lesser numbers affiliated with political science, anthropology and sociology, American studies, the fine arts, philosophy and religion. The courses are aimed at introducing a new method for the study of civilization to the institution at large.

The elite group represents, naturally, a greater number of courses per college with an even greater ratio of popularity. In only a few ways, however, does this group differ, in the proportions represented, from the larger group. Courses exist here more often for the training of majors; they include materials from a larger-than-typical variety of departmental sources; they are staffed more often by instructors affiliated with American studies departments; the teaching method is predominantly that of discussion led by a single instructor; and the organization reflects the topical at the expense of other methods. This group accounts for half of all American civilization tutorials. Otherwise the elite group reflects the characteristics of the whole; even where it differs, it only reveals tendencies desirable where well developed major programs are the rule and where courses, therefore, are subservient to the aims of the program rather than existent as ends in themselves.

GRADUATE PROGRAMS

Compared with undergraduate activity considerably less has been published on the subject of graduate programs and courses in American studies; the Washington Conference touched only indirectly on graduate activity; relatively few institutions have graduate programs. Therefore, the discussion which follows is based almost entirely on reports and statistics from a limited number of institutions. These are:

INSTITUTIONS OFFERING THE M. A. (but not the Ph. D.) IN AMERICAN CIVILIZATION:

Baylor University
Colgate University
Florida State University
Stetson University
University of Buffalo
University of Wyoming

INSTITUTIONS OFFERING THE Ph. D. (but not the M. A.) IN AMERICAN CIVILIZATION:

Harvard University
New Mexico University
University of Wisconsin
Yale University

INSTITUTIONS OFFERING BOTH THE M. A. AND THE Ph. D. IN
AMERICAN CIVILIZATION:

Brown University
George Washington University
New York University
State University of Iowa
University of Maryland
University of Michigan
University of Minnesota
University of Pennsylvania
Western Reserve University

Graduate activity also involves special summer work which will
not be discussed here (but see the section following the directory,
pp.146-49). Certain other institutions offer graduate work related to American civilization; this activity has been reported on in the individual directory entries and in the discussion of activities related to American
studies. Data from these institutions, however, has not generally been
included in the statistical summary which is based on responses from
those nineteen institutions named above. Graduate programs where
occasional activity in American studies exists, or where work related
to American studies takes place, are located at:

Cornell University
Mt. Holyoke College
Sarah Lawrence College
University of Chicago
University of Delaware
University of Texas
University of Utah

Chronologically the graduate portion of the American studies movement exhibits a less dramatic picture of growth than does the movement
as a whole. Undergraduate American studies programs had some beginnings, at least, early in the century; but they have grown most spec-
tacularly since 1950. Graduate programs came into existence more
recently (as late as 1930 there were none) and have grown, since then,
steadily if not startlingly. Six programs were established in the thirties,
eight in the forties, and five since 1950. To some extent, a cause and
effect relationship can probably be witnessed here, since the existence
of undergraduate courses and programs in the field was required before
the demand for persons with special graduate training in American civilization could be felt.

The administration of graduate programs has been treated under the general discussion of administration above. In some institutions, the graduate offering is administered differently from the undergraduate offering; but such instances are rare and not significant, and the general administrative picture in American studies covers the graduate portion fairly.

In their curricular characteristics, the graduate programs reflect some of the same tendencies as their undergraduate counterparts, while at the same time exhibiting some important differences. As with the undergraduate programs, the most frequent description checked was an "interdepartmental or interdivisional major including humanities, history and social sciences." Whereas about 72% of the undergraduate programs were at least partially described by this phrase, only some 53% of the graduate programs were. When this phrase was checked, the responder was asked to indicate whether or not a concentration in a single discipline was also a requirement of the major. In the case of the undergraduate program, only one-fourth of the institutions involved answered this affirmatively; whereas half of the graduate programs made this qualification. When one notes that the alternative descriptions of the major to the one above cited all involve a more rigid conformity to departmental influences, the distinction between the character of the undergraduate and graduate program becomes clear.

This distinction reveals the graduate program as less experimental and more closely allied to the conventional departmental pattern than the undergraduate program. Such compromises between conventional and interdisciplinary graduate programs as the double major, the major in a traditional department with a minor in the American area, the related major-minor pattern, indicate an unwillingness on the part of the graduate sponsor to turn the student loose without some clear departmental identity. Even when the interdisciplinary influence dominates, a strong conventional concentration is required in at least half the cases. No more than one-quarter of the graduate programs, then, have set up programs which allow students to emerge with advanced degrees in American civilization without also providing strong departmental emphasis.

In the past, at least, such a policy has been eminently justifiable. Students engaged in graduate work in American studies, as the survey shows, are preparing predominantly for careers as teachers. At least on the college level, as the survey also shows, appointments directly in American civilization have been unusual. Therefore, the graduate schools have obviously and justifiably felt that they were safeguarding the future of their students when they demanded, in addition to interdisciplinary course work and research, an easily identifiable affiliation with a conventional department. Whether graduate programs of this character are ideal or whether they represent only a compromise with reality is a judgment that this discussion is not prepared to make. Certainly, though, the rapid growth in undergraduate activity in American civilization during the present decade can be taken as an indication of increased teaching opportunities on the college level in American civilization as such. If, then, the combination of interdisciplinary with traditional work at the graduate level represents the long arm of necessity, the time may be approaching for a re-examination of many of our graduate programs. If, on the other hand, this combination represents a practical application of the American studies idea at the graduate level, then the present structure of graduate programs can readily be endorsed.

A report on departmental requirements in graduate work indicates that, as in the case of the undergraduate program, literature and history dominate. The notable distinction here is the relative prevalence of requirements in the fine arts and philosophy at the expense (when compared to the undergraduate program) of the social sciences. Of the eighteen institutions responding to this question, sixteen reported required course work in history, and thirteen in literature. Other fields were represented in terms of required courses in the following order: art (8); philosophy (8); architecture (6); sociology (5); music (4); religion (4); political science (4); economics (4); a social science option (3); anthropology (2); history of science and technology (2); and geography (1). Course requirements are generally not specific in graduate programs and many alternatives exist, so that these figures cannot be taken as absolutely representative. Anyone who reads through the description of these programs, however, will be struck with the almost universal emphasis on history and literature as the principal focus of graduate work in this area. When a third or fourth field is called for, it will usually involve more of the humanities -- either domestic or foreign -- rather than the social sciences (particularly political science) which appear so prominently in the undergraduate programs. Even when the opportunity exists, usually as an option, for work in the social sciences, one finds little evidence, in dissertation and thesis titles or in post-degree work, to indicate any important influence of the social sciences on graduate work in American civilization. In the light of the rising interest in the culture concept as an approach to American civilization (as evidenced at the Washington Conference), this may be a serious shortcoming.

Additional evidence as to the almost exclusive domination of the humanities may be had from several other sources in the questionnaires. Both as to courses added and courses needed in relation to American studies, those responding to the questionnaire laid heavy stress on literature, history, American civilization, the fine arts, and philosophy. In the combined areas of anthropology, economics, political science, psychology, and sociology, only one single course was reported as added to the offerings as the result of the American studies curriculum. And, in this same large area, only four courses were reported as needed! Whereas in philosophy alone, three courses were added and six felt needed.

The typical American studies graduate student has his undergraduate training in literature (13) or history (9), with some few from such fields as political science (3), anthropology or sociology (3), the fine arts (1), economics (1), and American studies (1). If he is a doctoral candidate, he will emphasize literature (9) or history (8) again (note the change in ratio toward history here), or possibly anthropology or sociology (1), the fine arts (1) or political science (1). If he goes on to enter the teaching field, he affiliates with a department of literature (10), American studies (8), or history (6) -- the only exception being one reported in sociology. These data are incomplete, of course, but they do represent an interesting cycle. Beginning with an undergraduate interest in literature, the student uses his graduate career to study almost equally in the fields of literature and history, returning to literature as a teaching field. The evidence is neither sufficiently clear nor conclusive for any positive statement to this end, but if any pattern can be observed, it must be this one.

The "honors" aspect of undergraduate American studies programs is not in evidence at the graduate level. Almost all institutions reported their curricula to be of approximately equal difficulty and extent with conventional ones. In only two cases was American studies deemed more demanding, while in one case it was appraised as less difficult than the usual program. Also in contrast to the undergraduate program, the graduate enrollment is predominantly male; in only three instances was distribution of sex reported as nearly equal, and nowhere was the female enrollment greater. The size of the graduate program is on the small side, averaging around ten at the M. A. level. As of 1957, one institution reported between 20 and 30 M. A. candidates; four reported 16-20; one, 11-15; one, 5-10; five, less than 5; and three, none. At the doctoral level, things are more flourishing. Over 50 candidates are currently enrolled at two institutions; one has between 21 and 30; three from 16-20; four from 5-10; and four, less than 5. Most of this numerical prosperity is, evidently, of recent origin; for there are no reports of over 30 doctorates having been awarded in the last five years at any institution. In two cases, between 21 and 30 have been granted during this period; in one case between 16-20; two, 11-15; four, 5-10; and three, less than 5. Of the sixteen institutions which furnished sufficient evidence to demonstrate a directional trend in enrollment, seven were static, seven increasing, and only two decreasing. Reasons proposed for fluctuations, however, were too varied to invite summary.

Graduate programs are both few in number and heterogeneous in nature. To plumb below the surface of a few generalizations would be to re-do the various directory entries, to which the reader is referred (as well as to Tremaine McDowell's brief but still largely accurate coverage of the subject, American Studies, pp. 42-47). The graduate program was founded, typically, in the 1940's; it requires course work and research in a number of fields but is also characterized by a strong concentration in a single discipline. Operating largely within the general area of the humanities, graduate programs stress history, literature, philosophy, and the fine arts at the expense of the social sciences. The student comes to this graduate work with an undergraduate background in literature, emphasizes history and literature in his graduate studies, and returns to literature as a teaching field. Comparable in difficulty with traditional programs, American studies graduate programs are of moderate size, especially at the masters level and, with two notable exceptions, at the doctoral level as well. Individual traits and special features of these programs are many and varied, and can be observed in the directory entries. Most of these important determinants have to do, directly or indirectly, with the problem of preparing graduate students in this field for successful teaching careers.

GRADUATE COURSES

Special courses in American civilization offered exclusively at the graduate level form a small, homogeneous group which can readily be described. There are but seventeen such courses, offered at ten institutions, although there are further indications of American civilization courses open to both graduates and undergraduates. There remain a half dozen institutions which offer graduate degrees without utilizing special courses at all, through a reliance on existing offerings plus individual supervision of the student's course of study and research. Six institutions offer a single graduate course, two offer two courses, and there are two cases where three and four special courses exist.

The homogeneity of this group springs, most importantly, from its singleness of function -- to provide the graduate student with the experience and equipment for understanding American civilization. More specifically, these courses often aim directly at problems of bibliography, scholarship, and interdisciplinary teaching. They are required, usually, of M. A. candidates or of Ph. D. candidates during their first year of residence -- many of these courses accommodate both groups. Focusing on individual research, they take up such problems as the contributions and methods of the various traditional approaches to the study of society. Either incidental or supplemental to this primary purpose, these courses often entertain special themes or problems -- such as the frontier thesis (Iowa State), urbanism and agrarianism (Minnesota), or the determination of values (Pennsylvania). The method of teaching rests on the seminar idea and on discussion led, most frequently, by more than a single instructor.

There are some exceptions to this general pattern, but they are few. Only one of these courses is offered as a general elective, and it is the only one which enrolls more than five students who are not candidates for advanced American studies degrees. In half a dozen instances the lecture method is used, but even here the seminar atmosphere prevails. At only two institutions (Iowa State and Western Reserve) has there been an attempt made to provide any significant coverage, from the point of view of content, of American civilization. And here also, the emphasis is on an examination of contributions by discipline and on the development of a method for synthesizing these diverse contributions. This is not to imply that the American civilization graduate seminar operates in a content-free vacuum where pure methods clash one with another. To be sure, examples are needed and are taken in the form of themes, issues, or periods drawn from the civilization; but only rarely does the seminar assume an obligation to cover specified portions of our past. Course offerings of the conventional departments are relied on to do this almost entirely in the graduate curriculum.

Departmental influences on the courses reflect much the same emphasis as do the programs themselves, although not so drastically. The social sciences are still under-represented in the subject matter of these special courses, but matters are not so badly out of proportion as in the case of the programs. For example, the content of courses by departmental criteria emerges in the following proportions: history (9), literature (8), architecture (8), art (7), philosophy (7), religion (6), sociology (4), history of science and technology (4), music (4), political science (3), economics (3), anthropology (1), and psychology (1). History and literature are once again in the van, this time all but overtaken by the fine arts and philosophy. Although the social sciences come at the end of the list, they are not far back proportionally. As for the departmental affiliation of those who teach these courses, the ratio can be represented as: history (6), literature (5), American civilization (3), political science (3), the fine arts (3), anthropology and sociology (2), philosophy and religion (2), economics (1), geography (1). Here the picture seems much better balanced between the humanities and social sciences.

There are many exceptional courses in this group in the sense of their interest as original and effective courses. Since the group is so small the reader may be referred, without inconvenience, to the pertinent directory entries.

Although the Washington Conference did not take up the matter of graduate courses, it is undoubtedly safe to apply the principle there expressed to the graduate level. The danger of any broad program -- graduate or undergraduate -- lies in confronting the student with a body of material in an unassimilable form. Traditional curricula provide for assimilation more or less automatically by sticking to the same general approach and organization throughout the course structure. In American civilization -- or some comparable program -- some conscious effort must be made to allow the student, under guidance, sufficient experience in fusing these various materials and methods so that he may, with confidence, continue to do so after he leaves the curriculum. This survey shows that the most common solution to this problem is represented by the graduate seminar. There are, surely, other methods of dealing with the problem of synthesis; without a special course to accomplish this, though, the program has a special obligation to produce in its students a coordinated educational experience rather than a relatively meaningless jumble. Since, in general, graduate curricula are more narrow than undergraduate, and since the graduate student possesses at least some background in his field, this problem is not so acute, in one sense, as it is on the undergraduate level. Insofar as the graduate student is attempting, however, not only an understanding of his civilization but also a preparation to teach and publish, this need for a serious experience in integration may be even more acute. And, since only slightly over half of the institutions granting higher degrees in American civilization offer special courses exclusively for their graduate students, this problem may well be the most significant that can be pointed out from the data at hand.

CONCLUSION

A history of American studies will unearth many possible and probable causes for its emergence and growth; statistics show that this growth has been an impressive one, of geometric proportions, which has taken place principally in the last twenty-five years. Colleges and universities of all types and in every region have adopted courses and programs in American studies; the prevalence of this activity has been especially notable in certain types of institutions (private colleges with non-religious support, women's colleges, larger universities) and in certain regions (the Atlantic coast, the Rocky Mountains and Plains). Even though there may be many reasons for the establishment of full-fledged departments of American studies, very few now exist and most programs are administered informally by the chairman of a steering committee composed of persons from various departments who are interested in the American area. Undergraduate activity takes three general forms: service (courses only), cooperative (a program but not a degree-granting program), and independent (a full-fledged undergraduate major). The last named is the most common and usually includes at least one special course in American civilization offered, typically, at the upper division level. Aside from the senior integrating course, the most vital is the introductory course wherein materials are selected and arranged thematically (or problematically) or to illustrate a cultural approach. The major program is drawn, otherwise, from established offerings at the college which are usually subject only to minimum rigidity (fixed requirements typically include only literature, history, and a special American civilization course, totalling very few semester hours) and capable of being adapted to a wide range of student needs and interests.

An elite group has been referred to from time to time in order to provide a contrast between this general picture and the situation where American studies activities are firmly established and flourishing. This smaller group has shown a tendency toward the establishment of autonomous departments, toward the inclusion of more varied course requirements from conventional departments, toward more experimentation in special American civilization courses, and toward the utilization of faculty trained in American studies. Aside from the characteristics which define this group, they have not differed significantly in other ways from the group at large.

Graduate programs and courses represent a much smaller group and must be treated, almost, as individual cases. As with undergraduate programs, the curriculum is drawn here from cooperating departments and synthesized with one or more special seminars. Whereas the undergraduate program includes a great variety of disciplinary approaches which lean, typically, in the direction of history and the social sciences, the graduate program, on the other hand, usually includes a strong emphasis in one traditional discipline and leans, by way of departmental influence, toward the humanities (history, literature, philosophy, and the fine arts) rather than toward the social sciences. In spite of this cautionary measure, there is still a fairly widespread prejudice against recommending that a graduate student take more than one degree in American studies lest he run an unnecessary risk of not finding employment at the hands of conventional departments.

The mention of employment brings up the question of what happens to graduates of American studies programs at all levels -- a question not hereto discussed. The answer, on the undergraduate level, is that the same things happen to American studies majors as happen to the graduates of any liberal arts program, with the exception that an unusually large percentage of them go into teaching. From questionnaire responses -- which especially on this question do not pretend to be complete or totally accurate -- it appears that some 27% of the undergraduate majors go directly into teaching; the next most frequent fate (about 16%) is the business world. The legal profession claims 13%; some 12% work for the government either at home or abroad; 9% go into such fields as editing, publishing, creative writing, or journalism; 8% go on to graduate work in non-professional areas; 7% go into social work or the ministry; 4% into library or museum work; and the remaining 4% can only be accounted for miscellaneously.

Between one-quarter and one-half of the masters degrees given in American civilization prove to be terminal degrees for the persons involved; and, once again, these degrees are used largely in the teaching profession. Numerically unimportant uses to which the terminal M. A. in American civilization is put include: professions other than teaching; the general field of journalism-editing-publishing; library work; and government work. If the graduate student earns a doctorate in American studies he will, once again, become a teacher in most cases. As a teacher his departmental affiliation will be with literature (38%), American studies (31%), history (22%), sociology (3%), economics (3%), or journalism (3%). If he does not enter the teaching field, he will work in: journalism-editing-publishing or creative writing (42%), academic administration (14%), government service (14%), library work (14%), public relations (7%), the ministry or social service (7%), and 2% in miscellaneous categories.

The predominance of the teaching profession as an objective for those trained in American studies is surprising only in the case of the undergraduate, if there. Students with the bachelor's degree in this field would enter, presumably, at the secondary level where the civilization approach is rapidly establishing its usefulness in connection with problems courses and core curricula. The fact that the American studies undergraduate is often female adds, perhaps, to this attraction between American studies and high school teaching. At men's colleges and at coeducational institutions teaching was also frequently reported as a post-graduate activity -- but it was mentioned only as a less popular alternative. That most graduate students in any area of the humanities and social sciences will enter the teaching field is probably a fair assumption. In the case of American studies, the surprising thing may be the number of occupations other than teaching which have been represented by holders of the Ph. D. On the one hand it is flattering to think that American studies may prepare one for so many endeavors; on the other hand, it is quite possible that the number of non-teaching occupations reported demonstrates the difficulty of securing teaching appointments at the college level directly in American studies.

Most of the noteworthy points arising from the survey have by this point at least been touched upon. As has been mentioned, this survey was not designed to answer questions about the "philosophy" of American studies; the Washington Conference, however, did journey into this realm and these excursions should be at least briefly chronicled since they passed through improtant territory. The two most persistent attacks leveled against activity in American studies related to the dangers of nationalism and superficiality. These two subjects were discussed at the opening session of the Washington Conference.

Arthur Bestor raised the public alarm most disturbingly on this first question in his article entitled "The Study of American Civilization: Jingoism or Scholarship?" "To a bigoted nationalist," he warns (p. 4), "afraid of the free and wide-ranging mind that compares and contrasts and judges for itself, how conveniently narrow an American studies program must appear!" The potential dangers involved here, certainly, must be admitted. Any attempt to account, historically, for the rise of American studies must include motivations rising directly from national self-consciousness. But the crucial question must be: Has nationalism only inevitably contributed to the impulse which brought these activities into being, or has it exerted a harmful influence over them once established? So far, Arthur Bestor admits, the "disciplined and enlightened scholarship of the men who have created these programs is the guarantee of their integrity." And Richard Shryock has pointed out that to ignore the study of the United States at this point in our history would represent a perverted and "lingering colonial-mindedness" (p. 37 of his article). Responses to the survey show that, except in the case of two or three institutions, no traces of chauvinism have entered into existing programs either in the intentions of those in charge of them or in the motivations of students who enroll in them.

Those who discussed this subject at Washington saw as the primary danger of this nationalistic focus not an incipient chauvinism but an unhealthy lack of perspective. Other civilizations must be studied, it was insisted, to provide the parallels against which the American experience must be measured in order to test its significance -- and the survey shows that a great many American studies programs either require or encourage the study of foreign civilizations on both undergraduate and graduate levels. Mutual reactions between American and other civilizations are often emphasized in the special American civilization courses. The important criterion here, beyond the mere exposure of the student of American civilization to other cultures, involves the closeness and usefulness with which these parallels are drawn. This problem, of course, rests with the instructor, and the importance of the instructor's preparation in areas outside America was heavily stressed.

While recognizing some potential disadvantages in the study of one's own civilization, the Conferees were not slow to point out certain advantages which pertain particularly to this sort of emphasis. First of all, there is the matter of expediency, the convenience of abundant materials, the absence of language and distance barriers, the common store of experience within the culture upon which all concerned may readily draw. The psychological need to understand oneself -- hence one's environment -- was held as a legitimate source of motivation as well as a constructive goal. Assuming as an ultimate objective the understanding of the civilizations of the world, present and past, there was nonetheless felt to be some real advantage in taking as a first step the study, in the spirit of the laboratory, of a society near at hand in both place and time. To use the evidence produced by the social sciences one must, to some extent, allow a contemporary emphasis; and the increasing abundance of these studies as applied to the United States offers additional justification for selecting American civilization as this laboratory. Thus, for reasons both theoretical and practical, the efficacy of the study of American civilization was upheld.

The other persistent criticism of American studies holds that in broadening the scope of materials as becomes' necessary for the study of civilization as a whole, the valuable depth of experience provided by more traditional disciplines may be lost. The discussion at the Washington Conference tended to treat this issue as a problem more in semantics than in curriculum. To insist that depth could be provided an educational experience only by following a single discipline through its particular arrangement of opinion and experience would be to limit the meaning of the word "depth." Cannot an equally important kind of "depth," it was asked, be provided by following a problem towards its solution regardless of whatever disciplinary boundaries or chronological preconceptions may be ignored? Thus the idea of American civilization may be especially suited to collecting data and experience around particular questions, themes, or problems, rather than to exploring relationships established within traditional organizations of knowledge. Any course of study, it was pointed out, has its limitations and pitfalls. The danger lies, in any case, in not being aware of these dangers; and the challenge, in the case of American civilization curricula and courses, lies in raising important questions and problems and in pursuing them carefully and logically toward their resolutions.

As final words, those of Richard Shryock, used to conclude the article already cited in this section, will serve better than any:

It is a truism that the nineteenth century was one which advanced learning through specialization; but that the resulting fragmentation of fields was carried to an extreme which threatened understanding in any large sense. The resulting effort, in our time, to reestablish synthesis has taken various forms.... The study of American civilization is one form of the latter process.

This is by no means an easy venture. It is small wonder, when one contemplates the complexity of modern knowledge and its division between many, firmly established departments in the universities, that the attempt to bring this knowledge together presents many difficulties. A somewhat paradoxical blend of enthusiasm and of tact, of zeal and of genuine self-criticism, are requisite if the experiment is to succeed. (p. 43)

Bibliography

Another American Studies Association committee under the chairmanship of Marvin Wachman (Colgate University) has compiled a bibliography of books and articles pertaining to all phases of American Studies which is, at this writing, slated for publication in the summer supplement of the American Quarterly (Vol. X, No. 2, Pt. 2) for 1958. The rough draft of this most thorough and useful bibliography indicates that there is no need here to go into the question in any detail. Hence the titles listed below refer only to works cited in the course of the foregoing summary.

Bestor, Arthur E., Jr. "The Study of American Civilization: Jingoism or Scholarship?", William and Mary Quarterly, Third Series, IX (January, 1952), 3-9.

Crane, William G., Chmn., Committee on the College Study of American Literature and Culture, American Literature in the College Curriculum. Chicago: National Council of Teachers of English, 1948. Pp. 32-49.

Davies, Wallace E. "From Sources to Problems: A Guide to Outside Readings," American Quarterly, VIII (Summer, 1956), 127-46.

Garvan, Anthony N. B. "The Present State of American Studies," Editorial Cultura (Mexico), No. 33 (June, 1952), pp. 45-52.

Grier, Edward F. "American Civilization Offerings in American Colleges and Universities," American Studies, I (October, 1955), 1-3.

McDowell, Tremaine. American Studies. Minneapolis: University of Minnesota Press, 1948.

Shryock, Richard H. "The Nature and Implications of Programs in American Civilization," American Heritage, III (April, 1949), 39-40.

Smith, Henry N. "Can 'American Studies' Develop a Method?", American Quarterly, IX (Summer, 1957), 197-208.

Spiller, Robert E. "Problems of Organizing and Administering Programs in American Civilization." Unpublished paper delivered at the Conference on American Civilization, University of Wisconsin, May 1-3, 1952.

Stone, James H. "The American Studies: Some Observations," American Studies, I (February, 1956), 1-3.

Taylor, George R. "Teaching the Art of Decision-Making," Journal of General Education, VIII (July, 1955), 254-260.

_____. "Undergraduate Programs in American Studies," South Atlantic Bulletin, XXIII (May, 1957), 1-4.

Index

Aaron, Daniel, 77; (ed.), America
    in Crisis, 19, 44
Abilene Christian College, 147
Adams, Henry, 75, 92
Adams, John, 92
Adelphi College, 7-8
Alderman, William E., 52
Alexis, Gerhard, 41, 42
Allegheny College, 8-9
Allen, F. L., Big Change, 132
Alma College, 151
American Studies Association
    (ASA), 1, 2, 4
American University, 149
Amherst College, 1, 9-11, 182;
    Problems in American Civi-
    lization, 10, 12, 24, 37, 50,
    78, 88, 90, 95, 113, 182
Ander, O. Fritiof, 13
Arizona State College, 11-12
Arkansas Polytechnic College,
    12-13
Arms, George, 110
Arnesen, Elias T., 72
Arnett, Claude E., 48
Augustana College, 13-15

Barnard College of Columbia
    University, 1, 15-16, 184
Barnes, Harry Elmer, and Oreen
    M. Ruedi, The American
    Way of Lif 48
Barnett, John, 97
Basler, Roy, 149
Baylor University, 16-17, 188
Beall, Otho T., 100
Bell Telephone Company of Penn-
    sylvania, 154
Bellamy, Edward, Looking
    Backward 2000-1887, 32
Bemidji, Minnesota, see State
    Teachers College

Bennett College, 17-18
Bennington College, 18-19
Benson, Mary S., 56
Berry, Mildred F., 66
Bestor, Arthur E., Jr., "The
    Study of American Civili-
    zation: Jingoism or Schol-
    arship?" 198, 200
Bezanson, Walter, 70
Biddle, Nicholas, 182
Billups, Sinnia, 59
Blewett, Edward Y., 109
Boller, Paul F., Jr., 78
Bolwell, Robert W., 36
Borrowman, M. L., 120, 122
Boston University, 149
Bowdoin College, 3
Bowers, David F., Foreign
    Influences in American
    Life, 64
Bowling Green State University,
    149-150
Bowron, Bernard, 1
Breathett, George, 17
Bridgman, David, 25
Brinton, Crane, Shaping of the
    Modern Mind, 37
Brooklyn College, 20
Brown, Stuart Gerry, 86
Brown University, 1, 20-22, 155,
    189
Brown, W. Burlie, 87
Brune, Ruth E., 79
Bryan, William Jennings, 182
Buffalo, University of, 90-91, 188
Burlingame, Roger, Machines That
    Built America, 134
Butler University, 1

Caldwell, Russell L., 115
Calhoun, John C., 92
California Institute of Technology,

22-23

California State Polytechnic
    College, 145
California, University of, at
    Berkeley, 91-93; at Davis,
    93-95; at Los Angeles, 152;
    at Riverside, 145
Campbell, Robert F., 2, 4, 24
Carey, Kenneth J., 71
Cargill, Oscar, 57
Carnegie Corporation, 4, 5, 16,
    19, 23, 89, 155
Center for Information on
    America, 153-154
Chase, Stuart, Proper Study of
    Mankind, 47
Chatham College, 151
Chattanooga, University of,
    145, 147
Chicago, University of, 145-146,
    189
Cincinnati, University of, 152
Clark, Dora Mae, 140
Clark University, 2, 24-25
Cleaver, Charles G., 39, 41
Clemens, Samuel, 92; Huckleberry
    Finn, 73
Clough, Wilson O., Our Long
    Heritage, 125
Coberly, James H., 36
Cockroft, Grace H., 76
Coe Foundation, 88, 147-148, 149
Coe, William Robertson, 124, 143,
    144, 147
Cohen, Hennig, 4, 5
Colby College, 25
Colgate University, 26-27, 188
Colorado, University of, 152
Columbia University, 1, 15-16,
    29
Commager, Henry Steele, 67; The
    American Mind, 40; Europe
    and America Since 1492
    (with Geoffrey Brunn), 48.
    See also Nevins, Allan

Committee on American Studies
    Programs, 1-5
Constanza, Sister M., 69
Cornell University, 30-31, 189
Coyle, William, 141
Crane, William G., "Crane Report"
    (American Literature in the
    College Curriculum), 160, 200
Crocker, Stephen, 132
Cumming, Robert, 29
Curti, Merle, 67, 82, 120, 123;
    Growth of American Thought, 50

Davenport, F. G., 55
Davies, Wallace E., 4, 155; "From
    Sources to Problems: A Guide
    to Outside Readings," 182, 200.
    See also Manning, T. G.
Davis, George L., 80
Davis, Joe Lee, 104, 105
Dayton, University of, 95-96
Delaware, University of, 153, 189
Denny, Margaret, 114
DePauw University, 147, 151
Dewey, John, 92
Douglass College of Rutgers Uni-
    versity, 31
Dow, Sterling, 42
Duke University, 151

East Texas State Teachers College,
    152
Eastern New Mexico University, 32
Eastern Oregon College of Educa-
    tion, 152
Eastern Washington College of
    Education, 151
Education Directory, 1, 161
Edwards, John, 91
Edwards, Jonathan, 40
Egbert, Donald, see Stow Persons
Elias, Robert H., 30
Eliot, T. S., 92

Elizabeth City, N. C., see State
Teachers College
Ellegood, Donald R., 5
Emerson, Ralph W., 92

Federalist, 73
Felheim, Marvin, 105
Fishwick, Marshall W., 128
Fleming, Donald H., 20
Flexner, James T., Pocket History of American Painting,
134
Florence, Ala., see State
Teachers College
Florida State University, 1,
32-33, 188
Ford Foundation, 13
Fordham University, 34-35
Franklin and Marshall College,
145
Franklin, Benjamin, 40, 92;
Autobiography, 42, 101
Franklin, John Hope, 20
Frese, J. R., 34

Gabriel, Ralph H., 14, 19, 78,
84; Course of American
Democratic Thought, 37
Garrison, T. R., 12
Garvan, Anthony N. B., 4, 156,
183; "The Present State of
American Studies," 200
George, Henry, Progress and
Poverty, 32
George Washington University,
36-38, 189
George Williams College, 152
Georgetown University, 35-36
Glazier, Lyle, 90
Goshen College, 146
Gossett, Thomas F., 131
Goucher College, 38-39
Graf, LeRoy P., 116

Grafton, Martha, 50
Grant Foundation, 153
Greenough, Horatio, Form and
Function, 73
Grier, Edward F., 1, 2, 5, 78;
"American Civilization Offerings in American Colleges and
Universities," 200
Grinnel College, 39-41
Gurko, Lea, Heroes, Highbrows,
and the Popular Mind, 88
Gustavus Adolphus College, 41-42
Guthrie, A. B., Way West, 105

Hage, George, 2
Hague, John A., 2, 4, 84, 155
Hall, Courtney R., 65
Hamilton, Alexander, 92
Hampton Institute, 151
Hartz, Louis, 42
Harvard University, 42-44, 188
Hauptmann, Jerzy, 2, 4, 61
Hawthorne, Nathaniel, 82
Heffner, Richard D., Documentary
History of the United States,
134
Hemingway, Ernest, 83
Hilldrup, Robert L., 51
Hillsdale College, 45-46
Hobart and William Smith
Colleges, 46
Hofstadter, Richard M., Social
Darwinism, 84; American
Political Tradition, 84, 105,
134
Hollins College, 47
Holmes, Oliver W., Jr., 92
Horton, Rod W., and Herbert W.
Edwards, Backgrounds of
American Literary Thought,
14, 134
Hovey, Richard B., 133
Howells, William D., Rise of
Silas Lapham, 101

- 205 -

Human Relations Area File, 183
Humanistic Education for Business
    Executives, Institute of, 154

Illinois, University of, 96-97
Incarnate Word College, 151
Indiana University, 151
Institute of Early American
    History and Culture, 3
Iowa, State University of, 4,
    81-83, 189, 193, 194
Ives, Burl, Songbook, 42

Jackson, Andrew, 82, 182
Jackson, W. Turentine, 93
Jacobson, Norman, 91
James, Henry, 84, 92
James, William
Jefferson, Thomas, 84, 92
Johns Hopkins University, 151
Jones, Robert L., 49
Jordy, William, 1, 4, 155

Kamm, S. R., 137
Kansas City, University of, 99-100
Kansas State Teachers College,
    48-49
Kansas, University of, 1, 2, 98-99
Keller, Charles R., 139
Kennan, George F., American
    Diplomacy, 40
Kentucky, University of, 152
Kern, Alexander C., 4, 81
Knights, Paul A.
Koster, Donald N., 7
Kouwenhaven, John A., Made in
    America, 88
Krutch, Joseph Wood, (with others)
    Is The Common Man Too
    Common, 88

Lake Forest College, 152
Lardner, Ring, 83
Larkin, Oliver W., Art and Life
    in America, 97
Larrabee, Harold A., 88
Lewis, Sinclair, Babbitt, 134
Library Company of Philadelphia,
    153
Lincoln, Abraham, 92
Lippman, Walter, Public Philosophy,
    128
Long, E. Hudson, 16
Loretto Heights College, 147
Los Angeles State College, 148
Louisville, University of, 152
Lydenberg, John, 46
Lynd, Robert S. and Helen M.,
    Middletown, 101

Madison, James, 92
Manhattanville College of the
    Sacred Heart, 151
Manning, T. G., with D. M.
    Potter and W. E. Davies,
    Nationalism and Section-
    alism in America, 98;
    Government and the Ameri-
    can Economy, 98
Mansfield, Luther S., 139
Marietta College, 49-50
Mary Baldwin College, 50-51
Mary Washington College, 51-52
Maryland, University of, 100-102,
    189
Marymount College, N. Y., 151
Massachusetts, University of, 148
McDowell, Tremaine, 4, 105, 156,
    160, 166, 167; American
    Studies, 192, 200
McKinley, William, 182
McLoughlin, William G., Jr., 20
Meister, Charles W., 11

Melville, Herman, 82, 83, 92
Memphis State College, 152
Mercyhurst College, 152
Meredith College, 152
Merrill, Charles, 84
Merrill, James M., 138
Miami University, 52-53
Miami, University of, 103-104,
    147
Michigan State University, 145
Michigan, University of, 104-105
    189
Middlebury College, 152
Miller, Perry, 14; American
    Thought: Civil War to
    World War I, 37; American
    Puritanism, 84
Mills College, 53-55
Miner, Ward L., 99
Minnesota, University of, 1, 2,
    105-109, 132, 189, 193
Monmouth College, 55-56
Morgan, Edmund S., 44
Mt. Holyoke College, 56-57, 189
Mulder, William, 117
Mumford, Lewis, 19; Brown
    Decades, 84
Murphey, Murray G., 2, 4, 155
Murray State College, 151

Nason, John W., 67
Neumann, William L., 38
Nevins, Allan, and Henry S.
    Commager, Pocket History
    of the United States, 134
New Hampshire, University of,
    109-110
New Jersey College for Women,
    see Douglas College of
    Rutgers University
New Jersey State Teachers College
    at Upper Montclair, 145
New Mexico, University of, 110-
    112, 188

New Paltz, see State University
    Teachers College
New School for Social Research,
    145
New York, City College of the
    City of, 150-151
New York University, 57-59, 189
Niebuhr, Reinhold, Irony of
    American History, 87
Northern State Teachers College,
    59
Northwest Missouri State College,
    152
Northwestern University, 152

Ohio State University, 152
Ohio Wesleyan University, 60-61
Oklahoma State University, 152
Oklahoma, University of, 151
Oswego, see State University
    Teachers College
Ouachita Baptist College, 152

Pace College, 145
Park College, 2, 61-62, 169
Parks, Henry B., 57
Parrington, V. L., 78, 82, 84;
    Main Currents in American
    Thought, 138
Paul, Rodman W., 22
Paul, Sherman, 96
Peckham, Howard H., 105
Peckham, Morse, 154
Peirce, Charles S., 92
Pennsylvania State University, 152
Pennsylvania, University of, 1, 2,
    4, 112-114, 154, 155, 183,
    189, 193
Persons, Stow, Evolutionary Thought
    in America, 64; Socialism and
    American Life (with Donald
    Egbert), 64
Pettengill, Samuel, 147

Pochman, Henry A., 120, 123
Poe, Edgar Allan, 83
Potter, David M., 4, 5, 84, 142,
    167. See also Manning, T. G.
Princeton University, 3, 62-64,
    132, 155, 169, 181
Puget Sound, College of, 151
Puritans, 92
Queens College, 65

Randel, William, 1, 32
Rauch, Basil, 1, 15
Raushenbush, Esther, 74
Rawley, James A., 85
Reed College, 65-66
Reeves, John K., 76
Richardson, Lyon M., 134
Riesman, David, 84; Lonely
    Crowd, 40, 105; Individual-
    ism Reconsidered, 87
Ripon College, 147
Roberts, W. H., 45
Rochester, University of, 114-115
Rockford College and Rockford
    Men's College, 66-67
Rockhurst College, 152
Roosevelt University, 67-69
Rosary College, 69
Rose, Albert, 95, 96
Rose, Arnold M., and Caroline,
    Negro in America, 101
Rourke, Constance, 84; Roots of
    American Culture, 88;
    American Humor, 105
Rudolph, C. Frederick, 139
Rusk, W. S., 129
Rutgers University, 31, 70-71

St. Augustine's College, 152
St. Bonaventure University, 152
St. Catherine, College of, 27-29
St. Francis College, 145
St. Mary's University, 71-72

San Francisco State College, 3,
    72-74
Santayana, George, 19, 84, 92
Sarah Lawrence College, 74-75,
    189
Schlesinger, Arthur M., Jr.,
    Age of Jackson, 101
Schmidt, George P., 31
Scranton, University of, 145
Scripps College, 146
Scudder, Townsend, 153
Sears, Lawrence, 53
Sellinger, Rev. Joseph A.,
    S. J., 35
Sheehan, Donald, 77
Shryock, Richard H., 156, 166,
    167; "The Nature and Impli-
    cations of Programs in Amer-
    ican Civilization," 198-200
Silveus, Marian, 123
Skidmore College, 76
Sloan Foundation, 145
Small, Miriam R., 129
Smart, George K., 103
Smith College, 77-78
Smith, Henry Nash, 44, 158; "Can
    'American Studies' Develop
    a Method?" 200
Smith, James Ward, 62, 64
South Carolina, University of,
    147
Southern California, University
    of, 115-116
Southern Illinois University, 152
Southern Methodist University,
    78-79
Southern Oregon College of
    Education, 153
Southwestern University, 153
Spencer, B. T., 60
Spiller, Robert E., 1, 4, 5, 112,
    158, 164, 166; "Problems of
    Organizing and Administering
    Programs in American Civili-
    zation," 200

Stanford University, 147
State Teachers College at Bemidji, Minnesota, 79-80
State Teachers College at Elizabeth City, N. C., 80-81
State Teachers College at Florence, Alabama, 152
State University Teachers College, at New Paltz, N. Y., 150; at Oswego, N. Y., 152
Stetson University, 2, 84-85, 155, 188
Stone, James H., 3, 4, 72, 158, 170; "The American Studies: Some Observations," 201
Susman, Warren I., 65
Sweet Briar College, 85-86
Syracuse University, 86-87

Taft, Kendall B., 67
Tampa, University of, 152
Tarkio College, 152
Taylor, George Rogers, 1, 2, 4, 5, 9, 11, 156; "Teaching the Art of Decision Making," 182, 201; "Undergraduate Programs in American Studies," 201
Taylor, Ross M., 119
Tennessee, University of, 116-117
Teresa, Sister, 27
Texas Christian University, 153
Texas Technological College, 152
Texas, University of, 150, 153, 189
Thoreau, Henry D., 92; Walden, 101
Thorp, Willard, 5; American Issues (with Merle Curti and Carlos Baker), 78
Tocqueville, Alexis de, 82, 84, 92; Democracy in America, 101
Trinity College (Washington, D. C.), 147

Trinity University (Texas), 152
Tulane University, 87-88, 147
Tunnard, Christopher, and Henry H. Reed, American Skyline, 134
Turner, Ralph J., 84
Turner, Susan J., 126
Tuskegee Institute, 147
Twain, Mark, see Samuel Clemens
Tyler, Moses Coit, 157

Union College, 88-89
Utah State Agricultural College, 150
Utah, University of, 117-119, 189

Vassar College, 126-128
Veblen, Thorstein, 75, 157; Theory of the Leisure Class, 101

Wachman, Marvin, 26, 27, 200
Walker, Franklin, 53
Walker, Robert H., 3, 4, 124
Ward, John W., 3, 4, 155; Special Program in American Civilization at Princeton, 181
Ward, Lester Frank, 157
Washburn, Wilcomb E., 3, 4
Washington and Lee University, 128-129
Washington Conference on American Studies, 4, 5, 155, 158, 167-176, 181-186, 191, 194, 197-199
Washington, State College of, 152
Washington, University of, 146, 148
Wells College, 129-131
Welter, Rush, 18
Wesleyan College, 131-132
West, B. June, 32

West Virginia University, 132-133
West Virginia Wesleyan University, 147
Western College for Women, 151
Western Humanities Review, 118
Western Illinois State College, 152
Western Maryland College, 133-134
Western Reserve University, 134-136, 189, 194
Westminster College, 153
Wheaton College, 137
Wheeler, Robert H. L., 4
White, G. Cary, 47
White, William Allen, Autobiography, 87
Whiteside, William B., 3, 4
Whitman, Walt, 92
Whittier College, 138
Wichita, University of, 119-120
Williams College, 139-140
Wilson College, 140-141
Winterthur Program in Early American Culture, 153
Wisconsin, University of, at Madison, 120-123, 188; at Milwaukee, 123-124
Wish, Harvey, Society and Thought in America, 120
Wittenberg College, 141-142
Woodress, James, 1
Wooster, College of, 147
Wyoming, University of, 3, 4, 124-126, 147, 149, 188

Yale University, 4, 142-144, 147, 182, 183, 188

Due